WAHIDA CLARK PRES. ✍ W9-BXD-981

W•CLARK
PUBLISHING
A STATEMENT IN LITERATURE

Pretty Boy Hustlerz

Part 1

Victor L. Martin

This is a work of fiction. Names, characters, places, and incidents either are the product of the author's imagination or are used fictitiously, and any resemblance to actual persons, living or dead, business establishments, events, or locales are entirely coincidental.

Wahida Clark Presents Publishing
60 Evergreen Place
Suite 904A
East Orange, New Jersey 07018
1(866)-910-6920
www.wclarkpublishing.com

Copyright 2014 © by Victor L. Martin

Library of Congress Cataloging-In-Publication Data:
Victor L. Martin
Pretty Boy Hustlerz
ISBN 13-digit 978-1-944992-76-7 (paper)
ISBN 10-digit 9871944992767 (paper)
LCCN: 2017904232

1. North Carolina- 3. Drug Trafficking- 4. African American-Fiction- 5. Urban Fiction- 6. Prison Life

Cover design and layout by Nuance Art, LLC
Book design by NuanceArt@aCreativeNuance.com
Edited by Linda Wilson
Proofreader Rosalind Hamilton

Printed in USA

Also by Victor L. Martin

Nude Awakening III: XXX-Rated

Pretty Boy Hustlerz 1 & 2

Nude Awakening II: Still Nude

Motive For Murder

Nude Awakening

The Game of Deception

For the Strength of You

Unique's Ending

Menage's Way

A Hood Legend

Anthologies

What's Really Hood?!

(with Wahida Clark, Bonta, Shawn "Jihad" Trump, and LaShonda Teague)

Even Sinners Still Have Souls

(with Darrell King, Tysha, and Michel Moore)

Dedication

RMW AKA Goldie = Wiz Khalifa & Charlie Puth
"See You Again"

- Acknowledgments -
Victor L. Martin

All praise to God for blessing me with this talent to write. Yet again I sit here in this prison cell, writing a new shout out for a book. This is an act that I'll never take for granted. I'll begin with a major shout out to my boss, Wahida Clark. I don't have enough room on the page to express the love & respect I have for you. Thank you for everything. I can't forget the editors with WCP. Because of y'all, you've made me a stronger writer and I am humble to work with each and every one of you. To my super group of friends that support me, Renita M. Walker, Jolene Paige, Yolanda Patterson, Kim Allen (my 1st typist), Anne McArthur-Burt, Desiree King, Patt McGee, Angie Moore, Felicia Moore, Chanail Paree, Tamika Razz, April D. Torain, Jennifer Willis (#1 fan). And with a new twist, I'll mention a few of my readers that support me on my Facebook page, Lissha Sadler, Saphia Inspire, Nahkila Butler, Rek Lvnlife Price, Nicole Alford-Pollard, Shawnetta Marie, Robert Marsh, Author LaToya Copher, Candice Murdock, Lynette Robinson, Richard Aswanu, Adrienne Overstreet, Tonya Wilson, Author Carlene Bowman, Donna Gatewood, Stacey K. Parker, Dell Banks, Lakeysha Reese, Jenny Jet, Kisha Green, Twandra Williams, Silk White, Joyce Veronica Burton-Harper, Vanessa Rodriguez, Jean Henson-

James, Kim Temple-Walker, Christial Inthlord Love, Latasha Williams, Ghason Davis, Tabeitha Pollard Mann, Marie Guammami Santiago, Delon Anoshi Hagood, Mizzdoubleg Ny'Jalea, Lamar Patterson, Barbara Grovner, Lisha Foster & IamStephanie Denise, thank you all for your support because without you there is no Author Victor L. Martin. And to sick with my custom to name a few of my readers behind bars with me, D. Williamson aka Fresh, Trap Money from East Spencer, Eric Dunn, Ashley Parks, Derrick Foreman aka Big Juss, Unique, Dice, Roberto Sanchez, Justin Graham, and how could I ever forget Perry Joines aka Black and a special mention to his sis, Joanne Joines aka Sweet P. A big thanks to my team of typist, Isaiah David Paul, Allyson M. Deese, Antwon Will Coxe, Claire Duncan and Jennifer Jimminez. And I must mention my fellow authors that are *write* behind bars, Ca$h, Kwame Teague aka Dutch, and Darrell DeBrew. And over the years the following authors have reached out to me, Joylynn M. Ross, J. M. Benjamin, Rumont TeKay, Leo Sullivan, T. Styles and Carl Weber. BTW, to all of my fans that enjoyed *Nude Awakening 1 & 2*, guess what's coming, *Nude Awakening 3*! And in closing, a special mention to my mom. It's all about you & I love & miss you so much. To my sisters, Angie & Tremika, my niece Janayla, my nephews Dominique, Ty Riq, and (RIP) Ty Kilo. The countdown to my homecoming is short. I'm humble in what I do and it's without an ego. To all of my readers, thank you for your support and until next time…Keep your eyes dry & Your heart easy.

Theme song for this book: De La Soul "Stakes is High"

P. S. I'll go ahead and put myself on front street and make a statement. When it comes to penning sex scenes, from here on out I'll let my writing show why I've earned the moniker aka Mr. Sex Scene. And if things pan out, I'll be teaming up with the lovely BBW Porn Actress Farrah Foxx #NudeAwakening3! And to all my haters. Just know that I'm like the dark side of the moon to y'all. You can't see me & that's not being on an ego trip, just stating the facts. And shouts out to Selma, N. C. and my old hood down in Liberty City (Miami, Florida). I will return.

-Author Victor L. Martin

Chapter One

Selma, North Carolina

June 11th, Tuesday

Present Time

"I can't keep living like this, Lorenzo!" Shayla Graham shouted with tears filling her eyes. She wiped them and stared at her boyfriend from across the bedroom.

"Do you know what I got in the mail today? More bills! Overdue bills that you promised to help me with. Every month you have a new excuse with your half of the bills. The rent is behind. My car is about to be repossessed. And nearly every damn night I have to feed our son some needles!"

"You act like I don't have no bills of my own!" Lorenzo fired back.

"What bills! How the hell you gonna convince me that you need some chrome rims on your cars?" She yelled. "We're about to be homeless! And all you do is front like shit is sweet when you know our shit is fucked up. You can't be like, Travis and rip and run the streets and blow money. What you need to do is maintain your home like a real man is supposed to!"

"Ain't trying to be like Travis!" Lorenzo shoved his arm through the ironed sleeves of his uniform.

"I can't tell!" Shayla glared at Lorenzo. "Ever since you got that job at the prison you've been trying to do what Travis do. FYI Travis doesn't have the responsibilities that you have. You have a son Lorenzo. We're about to lose everything baby. If I have to move back to Smithfield with my mom, where will you go? What? Back up to Michigan with your family."

"I'm doing the best I can, Shayla! I can't give you what I don't have."

"Something has to change. And it has to be now. Every damn day I'm having to beg for overtime at Walmart and nine times out of ten I never get it. I can't keep giving you gas money when my own damn tank stays on empty."

"It's not like I'm not trying, Shayla." He turned to face her. "I hate being broke all the time and living from check to check."

Shayla flopped down on the foot of the bed with her chin down. "This is driving me crazy! Why is this happening to me? It's the same problems every month," she murmured. "If I lose this home, I don't know what will become of us, Lorenzo."

"Shayla," Lorenzo called out.

"What?" She looked up.

"Baby, I know times are hard. But you have to believe in me. Have some faith in me."

"Believing in you and having faith in you isn't going to keep a roof over our heads. I swear I'm trying to stick this one out with you." Shayla softened her tone.

"Times get hard and you wanna break up!"

"I didn't say that," she replied.

"So, what was that shit about you not knowing what will become of us!"

Her eyes began to pool with fresh tears. She crossed her arms and looked down at the floor, slightly rocking back and forth. *Maybe I would be better off by myself. Just my son and I. But God, I love Lorenzo*, she thought with a hurting heart.

"Talk to me, Shayla. Where all this breaking up bullshit coming from? Over some fucking bills?"

"It's not just some fucking bills!" she snapped. "It's us, Lorenzo! Our life. Our present and our future. But you know what?" she shot to her feet and glared at him. "I'm willing to do whatever to keep this place our home! If I have to—" she paused to wipe her tears. "I'll go to Wilson and work out—"

"No the fuck you ain't!" Lorenzo butted in. "That bullshit ain't even up for discussing! You can dead that idea and I mean it, Shayla!"

"But."

"No! I meant what I said, Shayla. I'll figure something out, okay."

Shayla bit her tongue on the job opportunity in Wilson. Beefing with Lorenzo wasn't helping her issue. She no longer cared what he wanted to discuss or not. Shayla had a fix to ease the issue of her bills, and at this point, she felt cornered into doing it behind Lorenzo's back.

***

Lorenzo Watson arrived at Maury Correctional Institution with his troubles still pressing. The only good thing so far was being posted in the control booth from 6 p. m. to 10 p. m. Since lockdown was called at 11:00 p. m., it would only be one hour of dealing with the worrisome ass inmates. From his seat in the booth he could see all three blocks, A, B, and C. Each block held forty-eight grown men, but in Watson's view, it was nothing but a fucking day care center. For the next twelve hours, his goal was to sit on his ass and do next to nothing. He never gave the inmates a hard time and he was known to turn a blind eye on a number of wrong doings. As long as they weren't trying to kill each other or escape, Watson stayed in his lane. All he wanted was his two checks a month and that was it. Around 9:00 p. m., operations made the announcement to lockdown for count. As always it was ignored by 90% of the inmates. They wouldn't move from the card table or TV's until an officer came inside the block. Watson could've been an ass by turning the TV's off but that wasn't his temper. The three floor officers and the sergeant

4

started with C block to lockdown. For the next few minutes, Watson had to respond to his radio and pop the cells open for each inmate to lockdown. The task was the norm to Watson, dull and boring to be honest. When all of the dorms were cleared he scanned the control board to make sure all of the cell doors were secured.

"All cell doors are secured for A, B, and C dorms," Watson said over the radio.

"Ten-four," Sergeant Karen Parker replied.

Watson reached for his soda when the phone rung inside the booth. "North side control," he answered.

"What's up, Watson? You in the booth again tonight?" Officer Lisa Hart asked.

"Yeah and I hope to stay up here. What's up with you down there?"

"Just wrote up one of these nasty ass clowns down here jacking off on me in the shower! Wrote his natural black ass right on up! I hate that nasty shit!"

Watson laughed, "Who was it?"

"Um...Charles Pender in E-block. Seriously, not that I would fuck an inmate but damn, what happened to all these men with the solid talk game? First moment these fools see a woman in the booth they fly up to the shower and leave the curtain wide the fuck open. I see enough dick at home. Shit burns me the fuck up!" Hart griped.

"What time you gonna take your break?" Watson asked after Hart finished venting.

"Uh… around midnight. Why? What's up?"

"Just asking. Oh, where Dixon at?"

"Mr. Travis Dixon is in F-block locking the kids down which is taking forever because he's too laid back."

"Tell 'im to come holler at me after count."

"Boy, please. Y'all two are like brothers. You already know his ass will be down there to see you. But I'll relay the message anyway."

"Okay, thanks."

"Oh, and guess who got walked out yesterday on the other shift?"

"Who?"

"Williamson up on green unit."

"Word! Talking 'bout the white girl with black hair?"

"Yep. Her dumpy ass got caught in the storage room with the canteen man."

"Damn! How she get caught up?"

"From the inmate running his fucking mouth! He told one too many of his homeboys and one of 'em dropped a letter on his ass. She also was dumb enough to send dude some nude pics to his cell phone that was found in his cell. I tell ya, a man in prison will fuck any woman breathing. Now I know I can stand to lose a few pounds myself...but ole girl was obese!" Officer Hart rambled.

"Will she be charged?"

"I doubt it but her fat ass is out of a job that's for damn sure. I guess she couldn't handle all the attention she got in here and fell for the first line of game thrown in her direction. I ain't listening to none of the bullshit these fools in here trying to spit. Fuck that. Motherfuckers can't pay my rent or car note, ain't talking 'bout shit, and that's just keeping it real!"

"True." Watson nodded.

"Well lemme get my ass off this phone so I can call my girl over on red unit."

It's because we got an empty refrigerator. Watson thought. "Thanks, Hart and I mean that."

Watson ended the call with Hart aka Miss Gossip Queen. She was cool and easy to deal with and had trained Watson when he first started working. She was in her mid-forties, married with two kids and having an affair with Dixon. Plus she favored Oprah Winfrey.

At 9:23 p. m., Watson wrote in the logbook that the count was cleared. The control board lit up as each inmate pressed their call button for their cell door to be popped. It was an easy task, pressing a button beside each blinking red light. It took Watson under two minutes to let everyone out. Watching the monitor he saw the feminine guy in B-block sliding inside another man's cell. Up on the top tier, an inmate was gestured for the shower to be turned on. Watson flipped the switch for all the showers, then leaned back in the chair. Nothing hard at all about his job. Thinking of his troubles he realized he still had a better life than the 144 inmates in the three blocks. Any one of them would trade places to be free without a second thought. Watson had to come up with a plan to earn more money to keep his life together.

His pride took a beating by Shayla's words but all she had spoken was the truth. He had a family to support and was worried if he could man up to it. His first line of thinking centered around pulling overtime. It would force him to deal with that dumb ass, straight-laced sergeant on B-rotation. Slumped in the chair he tried to keep it together when Dixon entered the booth at 9:50 p. m.

Dixon and Watson were indeed the best of friends. Dixon had been a CO at MCI for five years and by all accounts, he loved his job. Both were on their pretty boy swag. At the age of twenty-four, Watson's dark tone and forever fresh haircut placed him in favor of Trey Songz. Travis, two years older, had a much lighter tone from his mixed race genes, set in likeness to Drake. Both stood at six feet even with an average build that suited their frames.

"Damn I'm tired," Dixon flopped down on a gray plastic chair beside Watson. He wore his state-issued Department of Public Safety cap like a fitted over his waves.

"I don't see how 'cause you ain't done shit." Watson joked.

"This unit couldn't run without me and you know it."

"Yeah right."

"You just mad because I get to do my own thang up in here," Dixon grinned.

"Hell, you fucking Hart so that shouldn't be a big ass surprise."

"Whoa bruh," Dixon smiled. "Check it, I don't *fuck* Hart... I only have sex with 'er so get it right. Now with my jump off, I fucks her sweet ass every chance I get and the pussy is hella good. For real, Asian girls do it better."

"That's TMI for me." Watson laughed. "I just hope you don't get caught up in your ways."

"Man, fuck them hoes. Why were you looking all spaced out in line up? Something wrong?"

Watson sighed. If there was anyone he could rap with and keep it 100, it was Dixon. "I might need to put in for some overtime to make ends meet. Bills are piling up on me, bruh."

"Shayla still working?" Dixon wondered. *With her fine ass!* Dixon secretly lusted.

"Yeah. But her checks ain't what they used to be," Watson complained.

"I'm glad I don't have any kids. Word up, I keep my shit covered all the time. But anyway how much are you behind with your bills?" Dixon asked as he removed his cap.

Watson scratched his chin. "'Round like five thousand."

"Man, working on B-rotation is gonna stress you the fuck out. Sergeant Miles ain't worth shit," Dixon stated.

"Ain't got no other choice, bruh. I got a family to support so all that other shit, I'll just have to deal with it and do me."

Dixon figured Watson's issues were bad since he had lent him a few dollars for lunch last week. "Man, if you do that they might move you to B-rotation since they are already short of staff. *Yeah. Get moved to B-rotation so I can dip over on the low to Shayla. Man, I'd love to see that tight little ass in a thong!*

"It don't matter yo. I got no other choice. I figure I can swing a couple of overtime shifts to get over this ditch 'til I get back on my feet. I'ma talk to Parker on my break and see what's up."

"Don't do it," Dixon shook his head. *Yeah, do it. Shayla don't need your broke ass anyway.*

"What! Are you listening, bruh? Shit is fucking crazy at home and my money is looking funny so–"

"Bruh, you have another choice." *Shit! I might as well help him out.*

"Oh yeah? Where?" Watson looked all around the booth then threw his arms up in the air.

"Can I trust you?" Dixon lowered his voice with a serious expression.

10

Watson crossed his arms. "What do you think? And how does that matter about the fact of me needing money?"

"Why do you think I like this job so much?"

Watson shrugged. "Is it these low self-esteem women you be chasing?"

"Fuck no!" Dixon stood. "Bruh, I'ma put you up on game 'cause I fucks with you. No bullshit... I trap this money every day up in this bitch."

Watson frowned. "You ain't on the block no more, bruh, and I'm talking about the streets. In a few eyes... we the fucking police... the man. Listen to what the inmates yell when we make rounds in the blocks. 'Block is hot. Man down.' So how are you trapping?"

Dixon's pride pushed him to prove Watson wrong. Once his pride was mixed with his ego it was a wrap. "How you think guys up in here be failing those drug tests and shit?"

"What does it have to do with me because I really don't care?"

"It can have a lot to do with you if you're tired of being short on money. Listen, I told you I was renting them rims on my Lac right? Well, I paid for them the same day with cash."

Watson shifted in his chair not understanding why Dixon had lied. "Those Rucci rims cost three stacks–"

"And I paid cash." Dixon cut in.

"Okay, you don't have bills like I do so you can–"

"That ain't the point, bruh. When I said I'm trapping, that's what I mean. This job is a gold mine and you don't even see it. When they took tobacco out of prison it was a blessing."

"How?" Watson was curious.

Dixon sat back down. "So I can trust you?"

Watson was hooked on how Dixon made money behind bars. The lure of easing the weight of his money issues was too tempting to let pass. If Dixon could spend $3,000 for a set of rims, then Watson wanted to do the same. "Yeah you can trust me. Now tell me what you got baking."

Chapter Two

Shayla glanced at her watch when she entered the dim strip club in Wilson, North Carolina at 10:42 p. m. A new tune by 2Chainz blared from the speakers as a shapely, topless, white girl worked the pole on the stage. A mixture of men and women parlayed inside the club with the latter catching Shayla off guard. This wasn't what she expected. The theme wasn't set in a 'making it rain' type atmosphere that flooded the music videos. The scene was calm with everyone laid back and getting their *fill* of tits and ass. Shayla viewed the thick, white stripper on the stage for a brief moment. *Dang, she got twice the ass I got. I wonder if I have what it takes to be a stripper.* Her presence in the strip club was being forced. She had no faith in Lorenzo and it all came down to her son's needs coming first. Making her way over toward the bar she gained the attention of the female bartender with a blonde Mohawk.

"I have a meeting with the manager, Shaun," Shayla shouted over the loud music while ignoring the funky stench of Newports and cheap perfumes.

The bartender lowered a glass to the glossy black marble slab. "You must be Shayla Graham?" she asked with a friendly smile. "You're here for the dancing opening."

Shayla nodded. "I um—"

"Gimme a few minutes and we'll talk in my office."

Shayla had only communicated with Shaun by text and email. She had assumed the manager of Twerk It was a dude. Dealing with a female placed Shayla in a more comfortable position to do what she had to do. Yes, she knew she was in the wrong to go behind Lorenzo's back but sometimes in life a wrong could make a right. For Shayla, that right would come in the form of money. As she waited for Shaun to fill a few orders she took a seat at the bar. Turning on the padded stool, she saw a new dancer on the stage in yellow latex booty shorts with a matching bikini top struggling to embrace her hefty brown breasts. She rocked her wide hips in synchronization to a bassy song by Future, which happened to be one of Shayla's favorite rappers. A crowd of young dreaded boys stood near the stage waving fists full of money while bouncing to the beat. The girl had a firm grip on the pole while twerking her ass to make it clap. Shayla took notice of the single bills massing around the dancer's stiletto heels. By the end of her set, she was butt ass naked and needed help from one of the stocky yellow-shirted guys to pick up all the money. Even if all the bills were singles, Shayla calculated damn near $300. Not bad for three minutes of work.

A tap on Shayla's shoulder pulled her attention from the stage. Shaun had found someone to hold the bar down while she motioned Shayla to follow her.

"You run this spot alone?" Shayla asked when the music faded out.

"Nah. It's me and my cousin but she's not here tonight," Shaun stepped inside her windowless office. "Want anything to drink?"

"I'm fine." Shayla sat down in front of Shaun's desk. *I can do this.*

"How many times have people told you that you look like Janelle Monàe?"

"I've heard that a few times," Shayla modestly replied.

Shaun nodded. "So you want to dance at my club huh?"

"Pretty much..."

"And you have no background in dancing on stage, and to be blunt you've never stripped in front of a crowd before, right?"

"Correct."

"Are you uncomfortable right now?"

Shayla averted her eyes to the floor. *I shouldn't be here. If Lorenzo finds out about this he'll blow up.*

"I'll take that as a yes," Shaun knew from past experience of meeting girls that *thought* they wanted to dance. "And to be honest with you, you have all the right in the world to feel uncomfortable."

"I... really need this job and I'm willing to learn." Shayla refused to cave in on her fear. With the extra money, she could get out of the financial hole that got bigger each month.

16

"Okay... we'll close up tonight around three and I'll let you hit the stage in front of my staff. If you can make it by them... you got the spot. So, can you hang around till then?"

Shayla nodded yes, committing herself before she could even think of turning the chance down.

"Did you bring any clothes to dance in?" Shaun asked.

"Uh, no. I didn't think I would be dancing tonight." Shayla admitted.

"Not a problem," Shaun told her. "I keep a bunch of outfits on hand and yes they are new. You're on the petite side so I'm positive you can find something to fit. Do you know your measurements by any chance?"

Shayla bit her bottom lip for a second. "Um... thirty-four B, twenty-five, thirty-seven and I'm five foot five without my heels."

"How do you feel about women being bisexual because I have a few working for me that dance to that tune?"

"I'm okay with it but I'm strictly for the D. I have an aunt that's lesbian so I don't have no phobia against... um, women, that like women."

"Glad to hear that because I don't want any problems up in here. All of my girls are levelheaded, so you won't have to worry about anyone harassing you over no bullshit. Do you smoke weed?"

Shayla began to fidget with her bracelet. "Not as much since I had my son, but—"

"It's not a problem," Shaun interrupted. "I love the green myself but here are my house rules. No drugs up in here period! And if I can't blaze one under this roof, then it goes for everybody. I run a clean establishment and I intend to keep it that way." Shaun told her.

"Do you have a VIP room?" Shayla became relaxed.

Shaun picked up an ink pen off the desk, slowly twirling it. "Yes, it's on the second floor."

"Will I have to do private dances?" Shayla asked after a brief pause.

"Not if you don't want to. But it will be more profit you'll be leaving to the other girls to earn. Take my advice and just get a true feel of this business."

Shayla nodded. "I'll keep that in mind."

"Well." Shaun stood and tugged the hem of her clingy green blouse over her waist. "I need to get back on the floor. You're free to mingle, or do you plan to leave and come back later?"

"I'll stay," Shayla queased as the butterflies swarmed her stomach. "Oh and one more thing. Will I have to go under a stage name?"

Shaun again focused on the strong resemblance that Shayla featured toward Janelle Monàe. "How about Lil' Monàe if it's okay with you?" Shaun suggested.

Shayla saw no reason to go against Shaun's idea. *I can do this,* Shayla thought. "I can work with that." She smiled at Shaun. "But without the lil."

"Good. Now let's go and see the outfits I have in your size." Shaun commanded as Shayla followed her out of the office with mixed emotions. Shayla's need of money pushed her morals aside. She had the looks to make it as a stripper but did she have the heart to do it behind Lorenzo's back?

***

"You got my money for this, Derrick?" Michelle, who stripped under the name Creame, asked as she shook her wide creamy ass in his face up in the VIP.

"Damn, you gonna really charge me two hundred fo' a shot of dis ass?"

She turned and sat on his lap. "I'm taking a risk as it is. You know Shaun will boot my ass up outta here if she catches me fucking. Now, do you want to hit it or not boo?" She smiled and pulled the pink bikini top off. She got the reaction she wanted when her natural, brown nipple, 36D's spilled in his face. Derrick sat up and kissed both of her nipples. She knew her white skin and thick curves gained lust and money, and she had no issue with flaunting all she had. She was

19

twenty-eight years old with two kids by two different men, one white and one black. For the last four years, she had stripped at three different clubs and she showed no signs of changing her career.

"How we gonna do this?" Derrick was eager to get started. He caressed her titties in the dark private curtained booth. "Damn! These motherfuckers soft as hell!"

"Easy, boo. But I need the money up front. I know you got it, so stop burning up our time. I promise you'll get your money's worth." she whispered as he played with her nipples.

Derrick rubbed her pointy nipples then lowered his hands to palm her jiggly, white ass. "Ai'ight yo. You got a deal."

Creame got off his lap then sashayed around the small table to shut the black velour curtains. Next, she told him to let her kneel backward on the leather crescent booth chair. She knew he couldn't last that long by hitting her doggy style. Tricking up in the VIP was routine for Creame. She allowed Derrick to nudge the tiny thong aside while she wiggled her ass side to side. Looking back over her shoulder she gasped when his condom-protected dick slid between her gushy pussy lips. "Ohhh…beat it up real good, baby!" She pouted her glossy pink lips.

With the music from the first floor competing with the sounds of sex, Creame took the dick with no regrets. Derrick stroked her hard and fast with one fist balled up in her long brunette mane. Her breasts slapped repeatedly against the seat.

Her ass moved in a nonstop ripple of waves that held Derrick in an opened mouth trance. In and out he pounded her bald thick lipped pussy with pure determination. Creame dug her two-toned black and white nails into the leather seat while Derrick kept plowing between her legs. Her moans were genuine. Rocking back against his hard strokes, a surge of pleasure raced up and down her thighs when Derrick firmly gripped her by the waist. Sex with no strings attached was a must for Creame. With Derrick, she was breaking him off for his twenty-fifth birthday. Or was it his twenty-sixth? She couldn't really remember. She knew only a few details about Derrick. He was VIP at the club, he liked white girls, drove a brand new Dodge Charger Hellcat, and had plenty of money. She had known him for three months at the most.

It took Derrick only five and a half minutes to reach his $200 climax. Rubbing her soft wide hips he stayed inside her warm hole until his dick began to soften. Creame wanted more, but it wasn't the time nor the spot to go all out to get her freak on. Seconds later, she was arranging her skimpy outfit over her plump frame when Derrick palmed and squeezed her ass. She giggled playfully as he told her how awesome the pussy felt. Deep down she was leaning toward giving up her number to hook up with him outside of the club. As good as the dick had been, she wanted things to stay strictly business.

"Happy Birthday," she purred softly with her arms around his neck. "I'll get up with you later and yes that meat was good."

Creame strolled out of VIP rolling her wide hips with each enticing step. At the bottom of the steps, she bumped into the head bouncer, Sayveon.

"You good?" he checked on her as he ogled over her barely covered breasts.

She nodded. "You got somebody to cover you while we handle this?"

"What? You talking 'bout doing it now?" he asked surprised.

"Why not. A deal is a deal, and plus I don't like doing it in your truck."

Sayveon licked his lips. "Meet me in the storage room in ten minutes."

"Cool," she replied, lowering her gaze to his crotch. "Just make sure you don't be late, boo."

Sayveon slapped Creame on her voluptuous ass as she strutted by him. Their dealings began a month ago when he happened to catch Creame tricking up in VIP. She pleaded with him not to report her actions to Shaun with a flood of tears. At first, he stuck to the rules until she said she would do anything to keep what he had seen a secret. Sayveon was married and had an unbroken code about fucking any strippers. With her job on the line, Creame offered up her soft-lipped fellatio skills to keep Sayveon quiet.

That same night she sucked his spirit down her throat in the back seat of his Escalade. From then on, she only did her hustle on his shift while he made sure Shaun wouldn't catch wind of her deeds. With each private session in VIP, she would suck Sayveon off afterward with little regret. She took the good with the bad but kept her focus on getting money.

Heading to the dressing room she was fully aware of the attention she drew with ease. For a white girl, most people assumed her 36D-24-47 frame was fake. She paid the haters no mind at all. Creame got down for hers and another bitch couldn't tell her otherwise.

She waved to a few men that she knew by their first names only. She blew a pouty kiss at one of her steady supporters seated at a table near the stage. She could always depend on Louis to tip her with tens or twenties. The music rocked the club and the lights stayed low. A hand palmed her bare ass when she breezed through a group of D-boys. She smiled, knowing a bitchy attitude wasn't her stance. "Don't grab what you can't handle," she teased without stopping. Creame yearned for the attention which would only turn to more money. It was her drive, her hustle.

Reaching the dressing room she spotted an unfamiliar girl standing near the rack of racy outfits. "Hi. Who are you?" Creame asked when she closed the door behind her.

Shayla turned. "I'm Shayla. I'm just looking for something to wear."

"Oh okay." Creame headed for her booth. "Shaun told me about you yesterday. You need any help?"

Shayla shrugged. "I guess."

Creame flopped her wide ass on the stool then spun around to face Shayla with a friendly smile. "My bad. My name is Michelle, but under this roof, I go by Creame."

"Nice to meet you." Shayla felt a bit insecure as she made note of Creame's prominent hips and an extra-large ass. Not only did she compare Creame's frame to a video vixen, she also had a beautiful face. In Shayla's opinion, Creame sorta favored Iggy Azalea, only thicker in all the right places.

"So you're trying to get a job here?" Creame inquired as she pulling her top off.

"Yep," Shayla replied, unfazed by Creame undressing in front of her. A second later she realized that Creame was the girl she saw on stage when she first came in.

"Listen, I'm not a hater, so if you're down, I'll school ya to this biz." Creame offered.

Shayla nodded but made it a point not to be so trusting toward Creame. Her goal was set on making money, not gaining any new friends.

Chapter Three

"Man, ain't no fucking way you telling me the truth!" Watson replied after Dixon had told him the scoop on his prison hustle. The two friends were now alone in the small break room with the door shut.

"I'm not bullshitting you, bruh," Dixon placed a slice of pizza in the microwave. "Shit is sweet if you know how to move, and you can best believe I'm not the only mutha fucking officer that's hustling behind these walls."

Watson took a sip of his soda then stared at Dixon. "What if you get caught?"

Dixon sighed. "Don't think of failure before chance. It ain't like I jumped head first without doing my homework."

"Okay… you said you make bread by bringing shit in, right? But how do you get paid? This is a cashless camp."

"C'mon Watson. I know you ain't that slow, man damn."

"I got your slow right here!" Watson replied sticking up his middle finger.

"Getting paid ain't a problem so trust me on that," Dixon explained.

"And you really made a thousand last week?"

"Yep and it's tax-free."

"Man I don't know," Watson was full of doubt.

"I've been doing this for three years and don't have no regrets. I know how to move and I don't fuck with any and everybody. Half of these so-called gangstas will snitch and tap out as soon as shit get hot." Dixon further explained. "Half of these dumb ass bitches that get walked up outta here is due to their own fuck up. Fucking with the wrong type of nigga."

"Man...I'm not feeling the idea of being a mule for an inmate." Watson battled with the idea.

Dixon shook his head. "Bruh! Did you even listen to anything I've been telling you? I'm not a mule for nobody! I do my shit direct sale. I'm the boss up in this bitch."

"And you want me to help you?"

"Nah," Dixon grinned. "I'll be helping you. Besides, I'm not a greedy ass dude. If you roll with me you'll see it's enough cheddar to go around."

Watson twisted the cap back on his drink. *Damn... a grand in one week. I could use that bread for real.* "Okay... I'm down for whatever."

BING the microwave beeped.

"Say no more, bruh. After our break is over I'll introduce you to someone." Dixon removed his pizza out of the microwave.

***

Victor L. Martin

Dixon knew the hustle inside the prison from top to bottom. Damn near any and everything was triple the value tenfold behind bars. A pack of Newports went for $50. That was viewed as selling weight. If it was broken down to rollups at $2 a piece, the breakdown moved the profit up to $120. Three nice $2 rollups per twenty cigarettes could be earned per pack. An ounce of Loud weed went for $800. A cheap prepaid $20 cell phone jumped up to $300.

Dixon had told Watson the truth about being the boss in his hustle. He was once offered $800 to bring in four small cell phones and two ounces of weed when he first started his job. Doing his own research he learned the true value of the drop if he had made it. $2800! Dixon realized that being a mule was chasing the scraps. He had a plan to cut the middle man out and be the man himself. If he snuck a cell phone in, he was getting $250 for it. If Dixon was anything, he was a true hustler when it came to getting money.

Around midnight, Dixon and Watson had to make rounds through the six blocks, A through F-block. Watson had A – C blocks. All he had to do was to make a walk-through and check each cell. If a window was covered he'd tap lightly to get a reply.

"Yo, Watson!" an inmate yelled after Watson finished his rounds.

"Yeah, what's up?" Watson paused at the base of the stairs.

"I need a sick call form, man."

"What cell you in?"

"Thirty-eight."

"I'll slide it under your door on my next round."

As always, someone shouted, "Block clear!" as Watson made his exit out of C – block. In the hallway, the night janitor mopped the floor while Dixon stood off to the side.

"You putting some wax down tonight, Mac?" Watson asked.

"Nah, maybe tomorrow. Ain't tryin' to stay out here too late," Mac replied, wringing the mop in the yellow bucket.

"Good, because that means I won't have to stand out here with ya." Dixon laughed.

"Where Hart at?" Mac asked. "Ain't seen her crazy ass all night?"

"She went up to the green unit with Sergeant Parker." Dixon flicked a piece of lint off his shoulder.

"Y'all heard about what happened to Williamson?" Mac asked.

Watson shook his head. "It's over for her ass."

"Part of the game when you deal with the wrong people," Dixon added.

Watson moved across the hall where Dixon stood, so Mac could continue mopping down the hall. Mac was thirty-eight and considered an old head in prison since eighty percent of the inmates were in their twenties. He had a life sentence and stood on his own and avoided drama at all costs.

"You ordering any new books lately?" Dixon asked Mac.

Mac glanced up at Dixon, then threw a weird look at Watson before he noticed it.

"I told Watson 'bout them urban books you be ordering and he wants to check one out when he's in the booth again," Dixon mentioned as Watson kept quiet.

"Oh!" Mac nodded. "I um, plan to order two new joints this week. I didn't know Watson liked to read."

Dixon shrugged. "You know how it be."

"So, you gonna turn my money order request in, or do I give it to Watson?" Mac asked going with the flow.

"Nah, I'll handle it. But in the future, it's all good with Watson, so it's some good info to know."

"Bet." Mac nodded. "Well, let me finish this floor to make it look good for the eyes on us."

Neither Watson nor Dixon thought of looking up at the security camera. They knew where each camera was and looking up at any would only make them look suspicious.

"What the hell was that all about?" Watson asked Dixon when Mac stepped inside the staff restroom to clean it.

"He works for me," Dixon replied smugly. "We spoke in code if you didn't catch on. Books are cell phones. He has two orders for me so that's five hundred I'll make. Two-fifty a piece."

"So what does he get?" Watson nodded down the hall.

"A hundred plus I gave him a nice book and a few other things that are priceless behind these walls. Mac don't lack for nothing up in here."

"And he's happy with the deal?"

"Yep."

"I hope you know what you're doing."

Dixon tapped the face of his G-Shock watch. "I gotta make a round right quick. And to prove I know what I'm doing, I'll show ya better than I can tell ya."

***

Mac wasn't in the position to challenge Dixon on his move to bring Watson into their hustle. On the issue of trust, Mac didn't fully trust any CO as long as he stood on his feet. To Mac, Dixon was no more than a crooked cop, but how could he judge? It was somewhat true about Mac not lacking for anything. Being that above all he wanted his freedom, he would never allow himself to be content behind bars. Mac's serving a life sentence in prison stood tall as a reality for his rash actions. Fourteen years ago three jack boys had run up in his crib and robbed him at gun point. He would have charged his loss to the game, but since his three-year-old daughter and

Victor L. Martin

baby mother were tied up during the lick, revenge was a must. His family and life hung in the balance of life and death for ten ounces of rock cocaine, two pounds of weed, plus $1,700 cash.

A week later, Mac tracked down one of the out of town jack boys and slumped him with a .40 caliber Smith & Wesson. On that day, Mac gave up his plate of freedom for a sour fruit of revenge.

Mac was still a hustler at heart and took each day as a challenge. His secret link with Officer Dixon was unique. Working for Dixon gave Mac an endless supply of all things money could buy. He told no one about Dixon, not even the guys he fucked with on a daily stance. Watson seemed cool. But being cool and being true to the hustle were two different roads to travel.

Mac did his job, mopped the floors, cleaned the staff restroom and break room, emptied the trash, nothing to sweat over. He was paid forty cents a day, a total of two dollars and eighty cents a week. Other than Dixon, Mac didn't fuck with the police. He didn't follow the norm with the new young batch of inmates. They deemed it acceptable to hang in a female officer's face and talk about bullshit! Most did it just to get in good, so they could have the green light to masturbate in their sight. They were open off a female that showed respect for the 'kill' as it was termed in NC. Mac wasn't cosigning on none of that bullshit, so he stayed, away from that crowd. At times, Mac hated to admit it because it proved how much of his life was wasted in prison. As a fact, he would admit that prison wasn't what it used to be.

"Yo, Mac. You already passed out the cleaning supplies to D, E and F block?" Dixon stepped out of the sergeant office.

"Yeah. I did it before I started mopping."

"You done with everything?" Dixon asked as he glanced at the spotless floor.

Mac nodded. "Hey, Sergeant Parker," Mac spotted her in the office.

"Hey Mac," she replied from behind her desk. "The floors look good," she said, sorting the outgoing mail. "Can you put down some wax this weekend?"

"Yeah, if you can get the warehouse to send me a case of wax."

Sergeant Parker nodded. "I'll send them an email about it."

"Aight, I'll see ya this weekend. I'm done for tonight." Mac nodded at Dixon and the sergeant, then headed back to his cell in A-block. He entered the block at ten minutes past two in the morning. Since he was a nighttime janitor, he had the okay to take a shower before locking back in his single-man cell.

The routine stayed mundane night after night, day after day. He stripped down to his black shorts and shower shoes, then headed to the shower. Tonight's shift was laid back, so Mac wouldn't be rushed to shower and lock back in his cell.

Twenty minutes later, he was back inside his place of rest. After hanging a sheet over the cell door window, he removed the damp towel from around his waist. No thoughts ran through his mind as he dried himself off. Minutes later he stood at the toilet to piss. Suddenly the door slid open and Mac was caught with his dick in his hand by Sergeant Parker. *Oh, shit!*

"You know you're not supposed to have any blinds up, Mac," she whispered but showed no displeasure in viewing his naked resplendence. She purposely blocked the opened space with her frumpy frame, in case another inmate happened to have their eyes on her. "What else do you need beside the wax from the warehouse?" she asked, removing a notepad and a pen from her pocket.

Mac hadn't moved an inch. Speechless, he stood in front of Sergeant Parker butt ass naked. He wasn't down with that gunning a female down bullshit, but this was different. To prove his point, Sergeant Parker had yet to lift her light blue eyes from below his waist. His dick had a mind of its own as it began to expand. "I uh…need a case of floor sealer," Mac said with his hands hanging at a dead weight at his sides. *Damn! She staring at my dick.*

"What about some new mop heads?" she asked with a grin.

Mac nodded, causing his thick-headed dick to bob up and down to Sergeant Parker's fantasying delight.

"Okay. I'll send the email as soon as I get back to my office." She jotted something on the pad with her focus planted on Mac's manhood. Clearing her throat she smiled at Mac, winking. "Be sure to remove the blind when you're done."

"I will," he turned to the side to give her a clear view of how her mere presence stimulated him.

She lowered her eyes and gawked at his imposing erect penis. As she slid his door shut, she made eye contact and mouthed. "Nice."

Mac couldn't believe what had just gone down. Sergeant Parker was well known to slug a motherfucker with a write up that tried her on that jacking shit. There was nothing attractive about Sergeant Parker. Hell, if Mac was free he wouldn't have given her a first glance for nothing. The deck was stacked deeply out of his favor. Yeah, Parker was out of shape and rated at the opposite end of being a dime. All that was true, but if given a chance, he would stick dick to her fat ass just the same as a size-6 sexy starlet. Mac slid his boxers on and crashed out on his bunk with his mind stuck on Sergeant Parker's brash actions. She had no doubt opened a line for Mac to play with if he moved wisely. *I'll fuck the hell outta her!* He thought, turning over on his side. Mac would play his role with Parker and stick firmly to ground rule #1: tell no fucking body!

Chapter Four

"Are you positive you want to do this?" Creame asked Shayla as they stood in the backstage area of the club.

Shayla closed her eyes lifting her chin. "Yes!" she resolved. "I have to do this for my son." *And all them maxed out credit cards I got to pay.*

Creame laid her hands on Shayla's shoulders. "Three minutes is all you'll have. Just relax, let the music move you. You'll be fine, okay?"

Shayla allowed Creame to school her with a quick lesson on Stripping 101. The funniest part occurred when she had to learn a few stripper moves from a white girl. Creame kept it blunt with Shayla. "Men love asses! Small and big. Make it clap and all you'll see is money fluttering around your pretty feet."

Within minutes, Creame became her helpful mentor and Shayla, her apprentice. A friendship formed between the two women that faced a mutual struggle that couldn't be ignored.

"How do I look?" Shayla asked for the fifth time in the last two minutes.

"You look fine, girl," Creame styled Shayla's ring of curls over her shoulder.

"Is my makeup straight?" Shayla pestered.

Creame frowned. "Now you're questioning my skills."

Suddenly, the lights on the stage changed from green to red.

"Showtime!" Creame encouraged. "You can do it girl. I know you can."

Shayla took a cautious step in the heeled sandals wrapped around her tiny feet. When she reached the wooden steps near the stage, she caught sight of herself in the floor-to-ceiling mirror.

With Creame's help, Shayla had her sexy, petite frame fashioned with a lime green mini two-piece bikini. The tiny bottom clung to her pert ass, and the top exposed the sides of her breasts. Her flat belly glimmered from a light sheen of baby oil, which was Creame's idea. *Just three damn minutes.* Shayla took a deep breath then giggled at a small notice taped up on the mirror.

Rich men tipping...Broke men looking

When the first notes of Wiz Khalifa's latest hit filled Shayla's ears she realized her future laid with the next three minutes. She took a deep breath and stared up at the red light. Grabbing the rail, she hit the stage, swiveling her hips with the beat under the lights with no worries over her head. Just as she neared the pole she lost her footing and fell on her ass.

***

"Girl, you killed it!" Creame later greeted Shayla in the dressing room. "I told you it wasn't all that hard."

Shayla flopped down on a chair with a smile on her face. Her emotions were mixed, embarrassed over the fall and ashamed over the act of showing her body to other men. All four of Shaun's bouncers had viewed Shayla's debut performance. Everyone gave Shayla props for continuing her act after her opening fall.

"You forgot to pick these up." Creame handed Shayla a roll of cash. "The guys liked you."

"How much is it?" Shayla realized she hadn't even noticed the money while she was dancing.

"Two hundred and fifty. Shaun didn't even take her cut."

"Did... she like me?" Shayla couldn't hide her excitement over what she just did.

"Girl, it's a wrap! You really showed some spunk after that fall."

Before Shayla could reply, Shaun strolled in with her jeans hugging her wide ass and thick hips. "I'm impressed." Shaun closed the door. "You'll need a little touch up on your eye connection with the crowd. But other than that, the position is yours if you want it."

Shayla nodded yes, clutching the well-earned money with both hands.

"So how do you feel?" Shaun asked with her hands on her hips.

"Relieved." Shayla's heart raced. *I did it! I did it! I did it!*

39

"I like how you did that little spin down the pole," Shaun told her.

"I almost slipped off," Shayla giggled.

"Don't stress it. I'm sure Creame won't mind showing you a few moves with the pole."

"Class is open!" Creame was excited for Shayla.

"Okay. When can you officially start?" Shaun asked as Creame began to change out of her tiny silver boyshorts and fitted tank top.

Shayla already knew she could only work when Lorenzo was at the prison. His shift ran for twelve hours from 6:00 p. m. to 6:00 a.m. She could leave an hour or so after him and be home and back in bed no later than 3:00 a.m. Again, she thought of her son. "I... can come back this weekend. Friday and Saturday, if that's okay."

"Perfect," Shaun replied. "And from here on out you'll be coming in through the back door. I'll send you another email on all the rules and so on, but other than that, I won't hold you up."

"Hey. What will her stage name be?" Creame sat at her booth in a pair of red panties.

"Um, how about... Monàe?" Shaun suggested. "She looks so much like Janelle Monàe, so let's make a play off of it," Shaun smiled. "Actually, we already spoke on it."

"I like it," Creame agreed. "Maybe she can even do her hair like Janelle Monàe."

"Nah." Shaun shook her head. "I want her to create her own style. What do you think, Shayla?"

"It's fine with me. I can roll with Monàe."

Shaun nodded. "Okay, it's settled then. Monàe is our new dancer at Club Twerk It."

"Yay!" Creame clapped. "And I think I found a new friend to kick it with!"

Shayla smiled. She did it. She was thankful for Creame, and she showed her true gratitude by offering Creame some money after Shaun had left. Creame refused the offer and looked at Shayla like she was crazy.

Per Shaun's request, all of her girls were escorted to their rides when they left the club. Halfway across the empty parking lot, Creame motioned Shayla ahead so she could speak to Sayveon in private for a second.

"You stood me up," she crossed her arms.

He shrugged his large shoulders. "Sorry. But I couldn't find anyone to cover VIP for me."

She pouted. "We can go to a hotel room if you want to."

Sayveon shook his head as he fought with the temptation. "You know I can't do that, Creame."

"Scared you might get a hit of this good stuff and get hooked?"

He grinned because she was dead on the truth. "You're too much. I'll have to take a loss for tonight, but keep that mouth wet for me."

"Always." She licked her lips, then blew him a kiss. "Goodnight, boy."

She met up with Shayla just as she got inside her gray Nissan Altima. "You got my number, right?"

"Yep. It's in my phone," Shayla said with the window down.

"Call me tomorrow. And remember, when I'm not up on that stage, my name is Michelle. I try to leave all this shit apart from my real life, and I suggest you do the same."

Shayla nodded. "I can't thank you enough for what you did for me in there."

Michelle shrugged. "It's just how I am. I don't hate. You'll see that as you get to know me."

Shayla assumed life was all good for Michelle aka Creame when she keyed the alarm for her ride. Michelle was rolling clean in a deep sea blue GMC Yukon resting on chrome. Shayla didn't envy Michelle. She could only admire the girl and her swag. At the age of twenty-six, Shayla had a ton of years ahead of her. Pulling out behind Michelle's Yukon, she didn't mind that she was starting from the bottom. Michelle had told her of all the money that could be made by stripping. Seeing the rimmed up SUV only pushed Shayla to stay focused on her mission. When her mind slipped focus she scolded herself. *I'm doing this to handle my bills. But a new ride would be nice.*

***

Michelle lived in a newly built three bedroom upper-class townhome located in Goldsboro, North Carolina. A bright full moon illuminated above her when she entered the parking area. She backed her Yukon into her reserved spot in front of her townhome at seven minutes past four in the morning.

A few minutes later she stepped through the front door and met her babysitter at the foot of the stairs.

"How are my kids?" Michelle asked as she turned to reset the house alarm.

"All tucked in." eighteen-year-old Brittney rubbed her eyes. "How was work?"

Michelle shrugged. "Same as every other night. Nothing worth talking about."

"Um, you got some mail today," Brittney said as Michelle dropped her Coach bag on the sofa. "I... think it's the letter you've been waiting for."

"Where is it?" Michelle asked dubiously.

Brittney pointed across the living room. "On the end table."

Michelle refused to let her stress show. "I'll read it later. I wanna see my babies right quick."

"Is it okay with you that I spend the night?"

"Sure. But I'm not cooking you any breakfast." Michelle kidded in an effort to mask her worried emotions.

Michelle quietly walked barefooted inside her kids' dimly lit bedroom. Yasmeen, her six-year-old daughter was curled under her pink and blue Minnie Mouse sheets in dream land. Across the room, her baby boy Rikeith lay on his back with the G.I. Joe sheets hanging off the bed. Rikeith was three, and the apprehension Michelle felt about the letter related to her son. Michelle Cooke had no problem facing the fact of being promiscuous. Through all of her ups and downs, she was aware of her faults, yet she had learned to live with them. Yasmeen's biological father was a married man by the name of Patrick Thompson. Without the courts assistance, he helped Michelle support Yasmeen but sadly, he wasn't making any effort to be in Yasmeen's life emotionally. After Michelle gave birth to Yasmeen she fell into a ditch of depression. She assumed Patrick would leave his wife and family for her. She was wrong and on the heavy side of being naïve. She gained weight nicely and in all the favored places. After numerous comments about her new voluptuous frame, mostly from black men, she started stripping. She relished the attention and the constant sex that came with it. Foolishly, she became too free with sex and dangerously lived a brief period of unprotected sex with multiple partners. She had to leave Greensboro, North Carolina when four black college students showed up at her trailer for a gang bang. Right then she thought of herself as pure trailer park trash. A week later she moved to Goldsboro and that was two years ago. The letter waiting for Michelle was her last hope of finding Rikeith's father. The first two letters had excluded each man she had requested for a paternity test. She wasn't looking for love. She just wanted Rikeith's father to be in his life. Every day she had to live with the guilt of her kids being fatherless. She laid the blame on herself and the unwise moves she made in her views with sex.

"I'm gonna do whatever it takes so y'all won't have to struggle in life," she whispered to her two kids before heading back down to the living room.

Brittney glanced up at Michelle as she came down the stairs. She lay back on the dark red leather sofa with a Kindle. "Victor L. Martin has a new novel out." Brittney turned the e-reader off. Michelle ignored her. Michelle had her hair down and her mindset for bad news. She didn't say a silent prayer as she picked up the letter off the end table. *Whatever it say... I'll still make sure my kids know that I love them.* Michelle tore the envelope open and paused at the familiar all caps bold font at the top left of the stapled two-page letter.

WAYNE COUNTY CHILD SUPPORT ENFORCEMENT

"Is it what you were waiting for?" Brittney asked as she sat up.

Michelle nodded. Taking a deep breath she unfolded the letter. Again she came across another familiar part of the letter. Only this time one name was different.

RE: *Paternity Test Results*

Michelle V. Cooke

Rikeith L. Cooke

Travis C. Dixon

Chapter Five

Selma, North Carolina

July 12th, Wednesday

There was little time for make-up sex between Shayla and Lorenzo when he got home at 7:20 am. His work schedule reared its head and stayed an unwelcomed conflict that lessened his private moments with Shayla. This week he had worked Monday and Tuesday with today and tomorrow off. His shift wasn't due back until the weekend, Friday, Saturday, and Sunday. The following week he would only have to work for two days, Wednesday and Thursday. It broke down to him only working fifteen days out of a month.

After a quick shower, he strolled out of the bathroom with a towel wrapped around his waist. Shayla was up, but still in the king-sized bed snuggled under the sheets.

"Is your mom gonna bring Alonso home or do I need to go pick him up?" Lorenzo asked about their two-year-old son.

"She supposed to drop him off this afternoon," she murmured with her face planted on the pillow.

"Shouldn't you be getting ready for work?" he asked taking the towel off to dry his arms.

Shayla dropped her gaze below his waist. "You coulda dried off in the bathroom."

"What if I don't want to?" He grinned down at her.

"You're just being nasty."

"And you must like it since you're smiling."

"C'mere." She sat up and reached between his legs. "Want me to make you feel good? Since you got it all up in my face."

Lorenzo draped the towel around his neck as Shayla worked her magic with her hands. He shuffled closer to the bed then reached for the hem of the pink tank top. "Take this off," he said as she stroked his penis up and down with both hands. "You know I love dem titties."

Shayla hid the heavy sense of guilt from her actions at the strip club. She met his request by quickly taking the tank top off. Taking him back inside her hands, she used her thumb to gently extract a drop of pre-cum to form from his tip. He moaned, sliding his hands up and down her arms. With the rising sun at his back filling the small spaces of the curtains he enjoyed Shayla's warm mouth. He couldn't bring himself to look down. With his eyes shut and head tilted back he stood firm with his erection easing in and out of Shayla's mouth. She had no porn star skills but Lorenzo had no complaints.

"Ahhh fuck! I love it when you do me like this," he moaned. "Mmm... just like that. Nice and slow."

Shayla kept both hands wrapped around his length as she massaged and sucked his flesh at the same time. Everything moved in a rhythm. Soft, wet slurps reached Lorenzo's ears, causing him to palm the top of her head. Her tongue teased the sensitive underside of his meat with each upward trip. When she suddenly stopped, he gasped, eyes popping open as if he had just learned how to breathe again. Shayla tugged her damp panties off with an *I want some dick* expression. The rushed movements made her upright titties jiggle. The second she was butt naked, Lorenzo was all over her. Shayla melted under the man she loved as he teased her sensitive nipples with his tongue while stroking her clit. Her nails sunk into his back when two of his fingers found the gushy entrance to her bald slit. Wanting to taste her sweet center, he licked both of her nipples then started his path down south.

"Not today," she moaned, pulling him back up, writhing beneath his naked body.

"Baby, lemme lick–"

"Fuck me, Lorenzo!" she blurted. "You got me so damn hot! Just shove it in me and fuck the hell outta me!" She parted her legs, licking his throat as he positioned himself above her.

Lorenzo threw her legs up over his shoulders then reached down to guide his growth inside her. Her back arched up off the sheets when he filled her up to his balls. He started out with hurried strokes that made her squirm and moan beneath him.

"Yesss!" she squealed, loving the way he tore it up. She felt his balls slapping against her ass each time he went deep. "Mmm, fuck dis good pussy! Gimme all my dick!"

Lorenzo threw his back into each stroke without pause. They kept fucking, only pausing to switch positions. Shayla couldn't muffle her whines when she took the dick doggy style. She panted with each stroke as his length slid in and out. Lorenzo caressed her nipples, fucking her thoroughly with sweat running down his face.

Shayla had so much love for Lorenzo. With him inside her she felt whole and complete. Gripping the pillow under her head, she begged him not to stop. He knew just how to get her off. Palming both of her ass cheeks, he continued to thrust between her watery, soft folds.

"Cum for me, Sha!" he smacked her left cheek. "Do it fo' me. Damn, dis pussy is so fucking good!"

Shayla's high pitched moans became muffled with her face mashed down on the pillow. She knew how Lorenzo enjoyed seeing her face down and ass up. His pace sped up. His grip moved to her tiny waist. She bit the pillow hard, squeezing her eyes shut as her body began to climax around his long plunging dick. She moved instinctively, rolling her hips to feel every inch he had to give. When he realized she was at her climax, he slid out of her then lowered his mouth to her wet tooted up pussy.

Shayla lost her breath when his tongue made lazy trips up and down the length of her outer pussy lips.

"Mmm…Pussy delicious!" he licked his lips, enjoying her juices all over his face. He spoiled her for the next five minutes by softly licking and sucking her freshly fucked hole. She wiggled it all over his mouth with ecstasy, pushing up goose bumps all over her sweet brown, pear-shaped ass. Her entire body shuddered the instant his fingers added some pressure up against her clit. He followed that act without warning by licking up the warm slit of her ass. Shayla pulled at the sheets, whimpering his name in a throaty moan that spurred Lorenzo. This was make-up sex at its best.

Later Shayla stood alone in the shower with the overdue bills on her mind. The recent sex with Lorenzo did nothing to ease her lingering stress on the issues she faced. The idea of telling him about her actions to strip crossed her mind. Even if he didn't understand, her mind remained set on making ends meet. Before she left for work she decided to keep her actions a secret. At least for now.

***

Lorenzo's deep slumber came to an end when his ringing smartphone forced him from his rest. Rolling to his side he grudgingly picked up his phone and viewed the screen. Seeing Travis' name, picture, and number he sighed and thought about not answering. Like most days after he got off work, he would sleep in until one or two o'clock. He assumed Travis would do the same.

"What!" Lorenzo answered without hiding his ill mood.

"Zo! Did I wake you up?"

"Fuck yeah! You know I don't get up this early, man. It's ten a damn clock!"

"Uh, is Shayla nearby?"

Lorenzo balled his face up. "Man what the fuck do you want? And why you keeping tabs on my girl? What type of bullshit you on!"

"Zo, I done fucked up and I need some advice and I know your ass can't help me."

"What kind of advice? And FYI, Shayla at work so your ass is outta luck homeboy."

"Damn!"

"Man I'm going back to bed 'cause I'm tired as—"

"Wait! Don't hang up!" Travis shouted in Lorenzo's ear. "Maybe you can help me."

"Can't it wait?"

"Man, hell naw. Just gimme a few minutes."

Lorenzo rolled to his back closing his eyes. "I'm listening," he said through his teeth. "Now what's up?"

"Yo... did Shayla ever take out child support on you?"

"Travis! Real talk, you startin' to piss me off. First, you wake me up talking 'bout nothing and now you wanna dig all up in my personal biz with my girl!"

"Nah, bruh it ain't like that."

"Then what the fuck is it?"

"Yo… I got a muthafuckin' letter from the child support enforcement office!"

"Child support?!" Lorenzo opened his eyes. "I thought you didn't have any kids."

"It's some bullshit!"

"Man, you tripping now. I'm hanging up."

"Wait! This… letter I got. It claims I'm the biological father and that the child support agency plans to take action. Can't this shit be wrong?"

"Hold the fuck up. When did you take a DNA test?"

"'Bout two and a half weeks ago."

"And now you tell me."

"Shit. I thought the bitch was on some bullshit and—"

"Wait, wait, wait! Nigga don't tell me you got Hart pregnant!"

"Fuck no! She got her tubes tied anyway."

Lorenzo laughed. "Lemme find out you got Sergeant Parker knocked up!"

"Man this shit ain't fucking funny!"

"It is to me. I thought you kept your shit covered when you be on your Don Juan trips."

"See man, you ain't shit."

Lorenzo kept grinning. "What does the conclusion say?"

"The what?"

"Look at the form and tell me what the probability of paternity is."

"Probability of paternity," Travis repeated. "Ai'ight, hold on a second."

"You better hurry the fuck up."

"Man chill. I got it right here. Okay... it uh... says the probability of paternity is uh, ninety-nine point nine percent. Since it ain't a hundred percent... that means I still have a chance of not being the father?"

Lorenzo couldn't believe Travis was that blind to the fact. "Um... this your first time ever doing a DNA paternity test right?"

"Yeah."

Lorenzo tried not to laugh. "Travis... ninety-nine point nine percent means your black ass is going to be paying child support buddy."

"Stop playing man!"

"Shit, you better be the one playing 'cause if that letter is real I can sell you a stroller," Lorenzo laughed.

"Fuck you! Shit ain't even funny yo!" Travis shouted.

"Hold up. Yo... who's the baby momma? Do I know her?"

"Nah. She ain't shit but a jump off."

"She can't be that much of a jump off if yo' dumb ass busting up in her raw diggity."

"The rubber popped for your damn smart ass info!"

"Sure. And the nookie was so good that you couldn't pull out."

"You know what? You ain't shit, Lorenzo."

"So," Lorenzo laughed. "I ain't the one 'bout to be paying no child support to a jump off so I'll be all the shit you want me to be."

"Why you always playing all the damn time! This some serious shit and all you wanna do is clown me."

"Man it is what it is. It ain't *if* the baby is yours, it *is* yours so all you have to do is man the fuck up and take care of your seed. Jump off or not, you can't ignore your seed and that's real talk."

"Damn!"

"So who's the girl? Do I know 'er? I bet she works at the prison."

"Nah," Travis replied sounding like his tires were flat. "You don't know her. Seriously, she was just a one night stand and my shit popped."

"And the pussy was so fire that you kept stroking."

"Hell yeah," Travis admitted. "Bitch was thick to death. Big nice phatty."

"Well," Lorenzo added. "I guess there will be a big change in your life."

Travis sighed. "I'ma call my mom. And don't tell nobody at work."

"Yeah, yeah okay. Look, I'll build with you later. Everything will work out."

"Easy for you to say," Travis murmured right before he ended the call.

Lorenzo had enough problems of his own to let Travis' weigh on his mind. Sliding out of the bed, he went into the bathroom to piss. While he stood at the toilet he saw Shayla's panties on the floor near the dirty clothes hamper. He figured she was in a rush to get to work and tossed her panties without much care. After he finished using the bathroom he picked up her tiny underwear then lifted the top of the dirty clothes hamper. Just as he dropped the panties on the pile of clothes, he spotted the fabric of a lime green skimpy bikini top. It drew his attention for two facts. One, Shayla couldn't swim and two, she only owned a few swimsuits and all were either black or pink. Curious, he picked the garment up by its thin tie string. *Since when did she buy this? And why haven't I seen her ass in it?* he wondered. Lorenzo looked back at the hamper and saw the matching bottom under a pair of his boxers. He picked it out with his mind running. She had to have worn the bikini recently since it was near the top of the pile. When he came home earlier he had showered with the lights off. Bringing the bikini to his nose he caught the present scent of cigarette smoke.

"What the fuck?" he muttered, knowing how much Shayla hated cigarette smoke. He frowned, dropping the bikini back in the hamper. Before the day ended he would question Shayla about the bikini, and he hoped the truth wouldn't hurt him. The idea of her fucking around behind his back had his temper running loose.

Chapter Six

Greenville, North Carolina

Travis used sex as a stress reliever and it became an added thrill when it was accomplished with another man's wife. Leaning up on his elbow, he tried to capture Lisa Hart's jiggling tits with his mouth as she forcibly rode him. Lisa had a wild sexual crave at the age of forty-nine, one that her fifty-six-year-old husband couldn't feed. Her ass smacked repeatedly against his flesh with the bed squeaking and headboard banging the wall. Travis dealt with Lisa because she was straightforward and honest. The sex between them stood without any emotions nor heartfelt affection. All she wanted was a solid dick and to be sought after by a man young enough to be her son.

Like always, the sex was raw between them. She felt free with Travis, doing kinky things with him that would freak her prudish husband out. She took it up the ass, mouth, and pussy with no guilt. Fucking Travis on the bed she shared with her husband was the norm. When her husband left for work out the front, Travis would creep in through the back. She bounced hard on his slightly curved erection, moaning at the top of her lungs. Lisa would never admit to Travis or anyone that seeing so many inmates' dicks at work could make her pussy turn syrupy. After riding him nonstop for fifteen minutes, she rolled off and used her mouth to please him.

Travis dropped his head back on the pillow as Lisa sucked his flesh. He hadn't told her about the paternity test results. His visit to see her was an attempt to push it from his mind.

"Mmm, I love this dick," she stroked it with both hands.

Travis watched as she took him back inside her hot wet mouth. She was okay to look at, but not the type to walk around holding hands. Her ass was plump and round and she had a hairy pussy that stayed moist. Her knowledge of sex allowed her to extend Travis' stamina until she was near her own climax.

Later in the living room, he took her hard on the sofa with both of her legs up on his shoulders. Her chocolate breasts heaved back and forth, matching the long-dicking strokes that Travis pounded between her thick thighs. Since she couldn't bare any kids again, she begged him to release inside her. She got so much pleasure and satiation from seeing Travis losing himself inside her.

After it was over, she didn't seek any pillow talk, nor did she want to hug up and cuddle. Since time was on their side, they took a quick shower together in the master bathroom.

"I'm thinking about taking my sergeant's test next month," she stood in front of Travis with her back toward him. The shower head petted her big double D's with a steady flow of warm water.

"What for?" he pressed his dick against her soft ass.

She shrugged. "Tired of doing the same shit, I guess. Hell, I've been a correction officer for almost ten years."

Travis reached around her and squeezed her slippery breasts. "You ain't gonna get brand new on me if you get your stripes will ya?"

She covered his hands with hers. "That will never happen. You know I can't function right without you." She smiled when she felt him growing hard again. "Are you coming to see me tomorrow? I got a new fuck flick I want to watch with you."

"Just call me when you're ready, but if something comes up I'll send you a text."

She nodded, then laid her head back on his shoulder. Their affair remained in secret with ease. Since they both lived in Greenville, and a mere seven minutes apart, their tryst was easy and convenient. Before he slipped out the back door, he treated her with a quickie in the shower.

Travis was greeted by the blazing midday sun as he strolled down the block to his ride. He dreaded the idea of facing the child support issue. His mom hadn't told him anything he wanted to hear. If anything, she was upset with him for his carelessness. When he popped the locks on his brand new platinum colored Cadillac XTS, his smartphone rang. By the personal chime he knew it was Lorenzo.

Assuming Lorenzo was still on some bullshit, he ignored the call and pulled away from the curb with the system thumping. Travis switched his mind to business he drove to WalMart to check out some cell phones. Checking the time on the CUE touchscreen in the center of the dashboard; 12:48 p. m. At a red light, he popped the glove box open and pulled out his second phone. The prepaid phone was unlisted with his job, nor was the account in his name. Turning the music down, he made a call with his hands-free Bluetooth calling system. When the light turned green, he pulled off behind a black Chevy Camaro with the phone ringing through the speakers. Travis counted the rings. After the sixth he would end the call and wouldn't try again until 3:00 p. m.

"Yo what up?" Mac answered on the third ring.

"Life and problems," Travis replied, switching lanes in the big body Cadillac. "I'm 'bout to go pick up the phones from WalMart. Yo, you know I can't get no big shit this go round."

"Man, just as long as it's small and can play some fuck movies ain't nobody gonna bitch about'em. So I assume you checked them pin numbers?"

"I did it as soon as I got off. Both were good, and I already loaded the money to my debit card."

"Ai'ight. Well, I got two more orders. Dude over on red unit sent me a debit card pin number for two hundred and another for three hundred."

"What he want?"

"A phone and five caps of powder."

Travis wouldn't have any problems adding another phone with the next drop. As for the five caps of powder, that was easy money. A cap was measured by a small chapstick cap. Travis could swing by his cousin's spot in Kinston, aka K-town and find five caps of powder residue on the table. "Text me the pin numbers and I'll bring everything in one drop. You need anything?"

"Yeah. Bring a box of KFC, and I need a new memory card for my joint. Oh, and don't forget to fill up that oil bottle with some exclusive shit."

"I gotcha."

"I'ma text you the pin numbers now, and I'll build with you Friday."

"That's what's up. And Mac, trust me on Watson. He's cool okay?"

"Shit, I'm in the back seat and just along for the ride. You know I'm down."

Travis took in Mac's last words after their call had ended. He began to press his thoughts toward Mac, feeling as if he was being played. As promised, Mac texted the two pin numbers and Travis checked them both. Next, he loaded the two new debit numbers to his own debit card. This week alone he would earn $900 and that was viewed as a slow week. The biggest commodity behind bars was cigarettes. Cell phones could last an inmate for as long as they didn't break or get knocked off with it. As for cigarettes, a pound would be smoked up within a week and Mac and Travis would supply all habits if the money was on deck.

***

Travis completed all his errands by 4:00 p. m. He had copped three prepaid phones from WalMart and scored enough powder from his cousin to fill eight caps. He figured it was a good time to hit Mac off with some work that he could bubble for himself. Travis wanted to reward Mac for being solid and keeping his mouth shut.

His thoughts of the hustle ceased when his smartphone buzzed. Since the Bluetooth system was on, the call showed up on his dashboard touchscreen.

"Shit!" he muttered at the picture on the screen. He slowed for a red light near the campus of East Carolina University, and he reluctantly answered the call. "Yeah?"

There was a brief pause. "Hello. May I speak to, Travis Dixon?"

"Speaking," he replied, listlessly. *What the fuck this bitch want!*

"Um… this is, Michelle. Did you get the test results?"

"Yeah."

"Were you planning to call me?"

"And talk about what?" Travis replied with a sour tone.

"A lot of things. For starters, I need to know if you're going to help me support our child."

"Ain't paying you a dime until I know for sure I'm the father!"

"Are you serious? Didn't you read the test results?!" Michelle raised her voice, becoming upset. "I was calling to see if we can handle things without the courts being involved."

"Too late for that," Travis muttered.

"So you're going to be an asshole about this?"

Travis didn't respond. *Bitch! I got your asshole.*

"I can't believe this shit!" Michelle's voice began to crack. "Do you even care!?"

"'Bout what?"

"Our son!" she shouted.

"Listen yo! You ain't 'bout to make a come up off me! What happened between us was a mistake, get it! Ain't no happy endings, so you can kill any ideas of us being a family."

"My son deserves better."

"What?"

"I said my son deserves better than your sorry ass!"

"Cool with me," Travis said as the light turned green.

"You know what. Fuck you, Travis. I really don't know shit about you, and I want to keep it that way. My son isn't a mistake! I don't need you... so kiss my ass!"

"Bitch, you can suck my–" He halted his heated words when he saw the line was dead. "Stupid ass bitch!"

When he arrived at his apartment he stormed up the steps and slammed the door behind him. Michelle meant nothing to him. He met her four years ago at a club in Greensboro. Travis pushed up on her hard and ended up with her in a hotel that same night. He couldn't front, the pussy was fire and when the condom popped, his strokes kept going. The one-night stand was that and nothing more.

Her next move worried him. Stressed, he pushed her from his mind and bagged the eight caps of powder at the kitchen table. When the task was complete, he returned Lorenzo's call.

"Yeah what up?" Lorenzo answered.

"Life and problems." Travis got up from the kitchen table.

"Yeah we got'em all, don't we?" Lorenzo stated.

"Well, I got ninety-nine problems and a bitch ain't one." Travis sighed and kicked his shoes off in the living room. "You still down with what we been building on?"

"No doubt. Ain't shit changed," Lorenzo mumbled.

"Damn. You sound like somebody stole your dog."

"I'm good. Just tired," Lorenzo lied. He wasn't comfortable with telling Travis about his suspicions of Shayla keeping secrets. "Yo, were you for real about that paternity test?"

Travis sat down, taking a second to gather his words. "Yeah. But it ain't nothing that's gonna stop my shine, you feel me?"

"How old is your seed?"

"Uh, three or something in that range."

"Bruh, you trippin',"

"Nah. But I refuse to let a trick kill my vibe. Look, fuck all that. Did you get a prepaid card yet?"

"I'll have one tomorrow and you said a Rush card, right?"

"Yeah. Make sure you handle that ASAP."

"It'll get done."

"Yo, will you tell Shayla about any of this?"

"Nah. I know she will trip so I'll have to figure out how to hide the money."

"Hell, just tell 'er you're working overtime and—"

"Fuck no! I'm not starting no trend of telling my girl some lies. Matter of fact, I'll figure it out myself," Lorenzo stated firmly. "Now back to you. Who is your baby momma?"

"Why you keep bringing that bitch up? You don't know 'er, so drop it. If I ain't stressing it, then it ain't shit to talk about."

"Ai'ight. Just remember that same line when your black ass call me asking for advice again."

Travis walked over to the living room window and looked outside. "I fucked the hell outta Mrs. Hart this morning," Travis bragged. "Tore that pussy up!"

"Wow, big deal," Lorenzo replied sarcastically. "I just hope I'll never have to say I told you so about fucking another man's wife."

"Ain't worried 'bout none of that shit. Uh, you still need that bread for your bills, right?"

"That's a stupid question."

"You can be an ass, you know. But being the true friend I am, I did a lil' sumthin' sumthin' for you."

"And what was that?"

"Go to the Western Union and pick up a money order for five thousand."

"Stop bullshittin'."

"I'll text you the info to claim it, and you don't owe me shit."

Before Lorenzo could reply, the doorbell chimed behind Travis.

"Hold on for a second, somebody at my door." Travis hoped it was the college student from across the hall. She was enrolled at ECU and played on the varsity softball team. She had a steady boyfriend, but she maintained an FWB, *friends with benefits* bond with Travis. The true blonde was a beast on the softball field *and* in the bed. Many of nights she had

68

pranced around naked inside Travis' bachelor pad after hours of kinky sex.

Travis felt his stomach shift when he took a look through the peephole. It wasn't his neighbor—it was Ron, Lisa Hart's husband.

Chapter Seven

Selma, North Carolina 8:10 p.m.

Lorenzo had a plan laid out to confront Shayla about the bikini when she got home from Walmart. He sat in the living room folding their clean clothes when she trudged through the front door looking tired.

"Hey baby," she dropped her car keys and cell phone on the kitchen table. "Where, Alonso?" she flopped down on the sofa beside a stack of folded towels.

"Taking a nap."

"I guess I gotta cook since you did all the clothes?" She smiled.

"Nah, I'm good. I took Alonso to Burger King today."

Shayla glanced around the living room and wondered what motivated Lorenzo to wash all their dirty clothes. He wasn't lazy, she just knew it wasn't a chore that he enjoyed doing. Hell, who really enjoyed the task, to be frank about it. What made her question his actions is that she didn't even ask him to wash the clothes. "You must be really bored." She picked up one of her T-shirts out of the pile of clothes by her feet.

"Nah. I knew you would be tired, so I went ahead and knocked it out."

Shayla folded her shirt, then laid it on her lap. "What's the envelope on the table?"

"Me being dependable," Lorenzo shifted through the clothes to find a matching pair of socks.

"Dependable about what?"

"Our bills."

Shayla looked at him, and then back to the thick yellow envelope. Without asking him any more questions, she picked the envelope up then glanced inside. Her eyes widened at the sight of its contents. "How much is this?" she took out a few bills.

"Five thousand. I told you to have faith in me, didn't I?"

Shayla laid the money back on the table. Now she felt even worse about going behind his back to strip for money. "I... never said I didn't have faith in you, baby, and I hope you don't feel that way."

He nodded.

"Where did you get it?"

"Does it really matter?" Lorenzo snapped.

Shayla frowned, caught off guard by his sudden attitude. "Are you okay? Am I missing something?"

He sighed. "Yesterday you were bitching about me being short on the bills, and now that I got it you wanna put me through a damn investigation!"

Shayla stood. "Hold up, Lorenzo. I don't know why you are tripping, but let's get one thing straight. I don't bitch about nothing! I just asked you a simple fucking question!" she emphasized with her hands on her hips.

"And I said it don't matter!"

"It does matter!" she shouted. "You promised me you would never sell drugs again when Alonso was born."

Lorenzo shook his head. "I'm not hustling, okay?"

"So how did you get the money?" She crossed her arms. "And don't lie to me, Lorenzo."

"Travis… he loaned it to me."

"And why was that so hard to share with me? We're a family, Lorenzo. It ain't about you or me. It's about all of us."

"I know, baby. I guess I just let my pride get in the way."

"Pride don't make you a man, Lorenzo. I fell in love with you because you are different. Look at where all your old friends are today. Yeah, they were balling, but that shit didn't last, did it?"

Lorenzo knew she was right. His old crew, once seven men strong, had all fallen from the top. "What did you do yesterday?"

He caught her off guard. "Huh?" She frowned.

He jumped off the sofa. "You heard me."

Shayla rubbed her forehead. "You're starting to give me a headache, okay."

"So you won't answer my question?"

Victor L. Martin

"Answer what?" she shouted.

"You cheating on me?" he asked with his heart pounding.

Shayla gasped, both hands covering her mouth. A look of disbelief covered her face. "Oh my god!" she muttered. "Don't do me like this."

"Do you like what?" Lorenzo got up in her face. "All I want is the truth!"

They stared at each other without moving.

"If this is some kind of joke, I don't find it funny, Lorenzo!" Tears filled Shayla's eyes. "I've never cheated on you, baby, so why are you hurting me like this?"

"Did you leave the house yesterday?"

"No," she lied before she even thought of telling the truth. *Oh God! Please don't let him know about what I did.*

"You must think I'm stupid. Either your ass went out somewhere, or you had somebody else up in here! Now which is it?" Lorenzo demanded.

She wiped her eyes, stepping back from him. "I'm not gonna stand here and let you accuse me of some bullshit!"

"Oh, it's bullshit, huh? Well, how about you explain this bullshit then!" He bent down and snatched up the bikini from under a pair of his jeans. "Who the fuck did you wear this for!" he shouted.

"I…" Shayla choked on her words, battling with the pain she would cause Lorenzo with the truth.

73

"I. What!" Lorenzo shouted and lost the reins on his temper. He took Shayla's reaction as her guilt for doing something wrong. He threw the bikini in her face with his eyes drilling her. Shayla winced, fearing for a moment that her man would hit her. She understood his anger, even if it was wrong. Just as she gathered her wits to tell Lorenzo the truth, their son entered the living room crying.

"Mommy!" he whined with his tiny arms up in the air.

Shayla rushed across the room and picked her son up. "It's okay, sugar. Mommy and daddy just talking real loud. No need to cry," she said in a soft soothing tone.

Lorenzo assumed his worst fears were true. Just the mere thought of Shayla with another man pushed murderous intentions in his mind. Acting on his only choice, he grabbed his car keys and headed for the front door. His anger caused him to ignore Shayla's crying pleas for him to stay. It had to be true, he reasoned. All he saw was guilt played on her face when he showed her the bikini. Leaving her behind was better than him putting his hands on her. His love for Shayla ran too deep to cause her any physical pain. He sped off in his ride, leaving Shayla and his son in the middle of the street.

***

Travis was in his bedroom counting money when his doorbell chimed. He glanced at his watch. It was late, 9:50 p. m. Since he wasn't expecting any company until later, he picked up his P227 pistol off the dresser on his way to the door.

He was still shook up from the unexpected visit from Lisa's husband. Travis had manned up and answered the door *after* he went and got his burner. To his surprise, Ron wanted his help to surprise Lisa for her birthday next month. Travis was cool with Ron, and last year he was invited to a cookout at his place. The second Ron left, Travis called Lisa just to make sure Ron wasn't on to them. She assured him that he had nothing to worry about. She also explained how Ron would always do some type of surprise for her birthday each year.

Reaching the door, Travis clicked the safety off the P227 then took a look through the peephole. Seeing Lorenzo standing outside his door, he tucked the gun away then unlocked the two locks.

"What up, yo?" Lorenzo murmured bumping his fist with Travis.

"Life and problems. Damn, Shayla let your ass outta the crib?" Travis closed the door and locking it.

"Don't wanna talk about her," Lorenzo replied stoically with his head down.

Travis turned the lights on as Lorenzo dropped down on the black leather sofa.

"Everything good my dude?" Travis took a seat on the matching recliner to the left of Lorenzo.

Lorenzo kept his head down with his elbows on his knees. "Shit crazy, man."

"You and Shayla got into an argument?"

"Yeah, but I don't wanna talk about it."

"Cool. So, you need to crash here or what?"

Lorenzo nodded then sat up. "If Shayla calls you, you ain't seen me, okay?"

Travis shrugged. "I got ya." *And I hope she'll call me.*

"Got anything to drink?" Lorenzo laid his car keys and smartphone on the low black and brass living room table.

"Um, I got some Grey Goose and some…"

"Lemme get that," Lorenzo grew a blank expression.

"Ain't no maids here. This ain't the Hilton."

"You got company?" Lorenzo glanced down the hall toward Travis' bedroom.

"Nah, not yet," Travis told him. "But I got this fly ass Korean chick coming from Havelock 'round eleven."

"I shoulda already known that."

Travis smiled. "That's the way playa's play, all day every day."

Later, Lorenzo sat alone at the kitchen table sulking over his third glass of Grey Goose. Shayla called him six times in the last thirty minutes. All of her calls were ignored. He figured she got the point that he didn't want to talk when she sent him a text.

I need to talk to you, Lorenzo. Please don't do this to me.

He deleted the text then refilled his glass. Sliding back from the table he felt a slight buzz from the Grey Goose. No sooner than he downed the rest of the drink did he realized he wasn't in no shape to drive home. Leaving his smartphone buzzing on the table with more text from Shayla, Lorenzo trudged down the hall to see what Travis was doing.

"Damn! You rob a bank?" Lorenzo asked as Travis stood by his bed packing a suitcase full of money.

"I told you our job is a gold mine," Travis wrapped a rubber band around $1,000 worth of twenty dollar bills.

"How much bread is that?" Lorenzo stepped inside the room.

"Fifty-six bands."

"Don't you know the Feds will…"

"Fuck the Feds. They can't take what they don't about."

Lorenzo lifted a banded stack out of the suitcase. "And you made all this by hustling on the job?"

"Yep. Been grindin' for mine, and one day you'll have your own plug. Shit, I laid the hustle to you, bruh. We got the upper hand and we got the constant demand."

"And fifty-six stacks is worth the risk?"

"Nope, but that is." Travis nodded toward his closet where two more suitcases sat on the floor. "I'm caked up my dude. I can pay off my full car note today if I wanted to. Now, I know I'm not ballin' on no Big Meech level, but I'm munching on this easy lick."

Lorenzo stuffed the brick of money back how he found it. He studied Travis across the bed. Travis looked nothing like a state employed worker. His jeans sagged off his ass, showing a pair of blue designer boxers. A gun sat in plain sight on the bed. Lorenzo felt the old rush of the hustle warming his hands. Seeing the money that Travis had and the ease in which it was earned, Lorenzo's mind was set.

"How long it took you to make all this?" Lorenzo asked.

Travis shrugged. "Uh, 'bout two years since I've really started getting on my grind. Hell, I know I done blew through some bread!" Travis picked up a second brick of cash and thumbed the crisp bills.

"Like I said before, I'm in." Lorenzo wanted what Travis had.

"You won't regret it."

Lorenzo nodded and told Travis he was calling it a night. He wanted to be in the bed by the time Travis' guest arrived. In the spare bedroom, Lorenzo sat on the bed in the dark. The Grey Goose had his head in a slow spin, and it didn't help to ease his pain and hurt over Shayla.

Sleep came in an instant when Lorenzo's head touched the pillow. The call of nature pulled him from the bed a little after midnight. Massaging his forehead he got up to go use the bathroom. It took a second or two to realize that he wasn't home and why. Leaving the lights off, he eased down the hall. Once he neared Travis' bedroom door, he heard a slow song pumping along with a constant tune of moaning and flesh clapping.

Lorenzo steadied himself against the wall. *I'm drunk as hell,* he thought when he finally reached the bathroom. He managed to take care of his business without tripping over his feet. On his way out, he leaned over the sink to cup a few handfuls of water against his face.

Just as he was about to head back to crash out on the bed he heard a soft feminine voice coming from the living room. Curious he went to see who it was. He was blown away by the sight he found. Sitting on the sofa was a lovely ass Asian girl talking on the phone. She had a slim build with a long, silky, black mane that fell deep pass her shoulders. The skinny jeans hugged tight against her thin legs, and the shape of her breasts was slightly visible through the brown thin blouse. His attraction toward her exotic looks was instant.

She smiled at Lorenzo, crossing her legs. "Hi, you must be Lorenzo," she said after ending her conversation. "I'm Kahneko."

Lorenzo's attention was diverted from the beauty on the sofa to Travis' 65-inch flat HDTV screen on the wall. A hardcore fuck film filled the screen, showing a group sex scene. Lorenzo stood rooted by the recliner until Kahneko grabbed him by the hand and gestured him to join her on the sofa. She was bold and direct with her intentions.

"I don't bite." She giggled, snuggling her body all up against his. "Can you watch this flick with me?"

The moment he joined her on the sofa he figured she wanted to bring the scene on TV to a reality. She stayed close up under him with her hand rubbing his knee. It felt too good to ask her to stop. Letting things be, he closed his eyes when her tiny hand slid up his legs. He showed no signs of stopping her actions when she moved her delicate hand across the throbbing lump under his jeans.

"Nice," she whispered, squeezing his erection. "Let me know if I'm doing too much."

Chapter Eight

Greenville, North Carolina

June 13th, Thursday

Lorenzo realized he went too heavy on the alcohol when he woke up in bed with Kahneko. Her nude, athletic body was a new element for him to seek his pleasure in. Guilt was hard to swallow, but the actions were already done. Lorenzo wasn't happy with himself for cheating on Shayla. Sighing hard he stared up at the ceiling, filled with regret. *I shouldn't be here.*

Kahneko whispered Lorenzo's name with her sexual needs still cycling. She nuzzled her soft lips against his neck while inching her hand down between his legs. Lorenzo closed his eyes as his body reacted to Kahneko's touch.

"Good morning, lover," she whispered as she circled her fingers around his dick.

Lorenzo responded to her touch, too weak to stop Kahneko from taking more of him. When her sexy face slipped under the green cotton sheets, he knew his will to resist her didn't stand a chance. She took him with her mouth, circling her lips around his penis while fondling his balls. The shape of her head bobbed up and down under the sheets. Her pace cruised slowly with gentle licks that had Lorenzo breathing hard.

After pleasing him for nearly three minutes, she came up from under the sheets and rolled to her back. She guided one of Lorenzo's hands between her thighs. No words were traded between them as Lorenzo threw the sheets back and moved on top of her.

Kahneko met his eyes with lust as she guided his throbbing dick inside her. A soft cry escaped her lips when his flesh stretched her open again. She gasped and threw her wetness up the length of his dick, forcing him to root deeper. Their pace started in a rush, each trying to reach that morning climax before the other. Lorenzo was mad at Kahenko for her art of seduction. He pounded her slim frame into the mattress, grunting with each firm stroke.

Beneath him, she took each push with elation, moaning from pure pleasure. Her small breasts jerked and circled. "Yes!" she shouted. "Screw me harder!"

Lorenzo sped up his forceful sex. In and out he plunged inside her tight warm pussy. His body became one with hers at the moment she hiked her knees up along his waist. Without missing a stroke, he tossed her ankles up on his shoulders.

Kahneko dug her gold nails hard into Lorenzo's arms. "Ohhh, baby!" she breathlessly moaned. "Mmmmm! Ahhhhh... fuck my pussy! Just like that!" She cried under him. His balls bounced off the back of her porcelain ass with each thrust.

Last night it was the alcohol that pushed Lorenzo to betray Shayla. Now sober, it tore at him that his actions and lust toward Kahneko stood the same. He pounded Kahneko with selfish thrusts to meet his needs. This was his way to salvage what small dignity he had left. With Shayla, he made the sweetest love. With Kahneko, he simply fucked her in an act of raw lust.

***

Travis crept in the hall with a slick grin on his face. He carefully twisted the doorknob to the spare bedroom to spy in on Lorenzo and Kahneko. Through the small crack, he saw Lorenzo fucking the shit out of Kahneko from the back. She was on her elbows and knees looking back at Lorenzo. Travis had called Mikki at the last minute and told her to bring Kahneko. From what he saw, his plan had worked out. The main thing that really caught Travis off point was the sight of Lorenzo fucking Kahneko raw. Easing the door shut, he turned and headed for the kitchen.

"Why are you looking all crazy?" Travis asked his jump off, Mikki.

"I think I got your boy Lorenzo in trouble," she replied with a sorrowful look.

"How?"

Mikki quickly explained how she answered Lorenzo's smartphone that was left on the kitchen table. "I thought it was your phone," she told him. "Anyway, his girl called and I freaked out and said Lorenzo was busy, then hung up. I'm really sorry."

Travis shrugged. "It ain't shit. But ah... let's not say nothing about it."

"But what if—"

"It ain't nothing so forget about it." Travis stared down at her bare titties. "C'mon." He slapped her ass. "Ain't done with yo ass, so let's get back in the bed."

Travis waited until he was alone in the kitchen. Thinking maliciously, he picked up Lorenzo's smartphone and pulled up the recent texts and calls log. He saw a total of ten missed calls and five unread text messages, all from Shayla. He opened the latest text that was sent a little after midnight.

Zo, please call me. It's not what you think. I love U more than anything and I would never hurt U. Call me so we can talk. Better yet, come home.

Travis stared at the text and wondered how serious the issues were between Lorenzo and Shayla. He had no intentions of helping Lorenzo maintain his relationship with Shayla. If anything, he wanted to slide up in Lorenzo's spot and get a shot at Shayla. With that in mind, Travis deleted every call and text from Shayla with hopes it would cause a certain breakup between Lorenzo and Shayla.

***

Victor L. Martin

Lorenzo later stood in the shower with Kahneko gently washing his chest. Her natural beauty and noticeable Asian features drew Lorenzo closer with each second he spent with her.

"So, you have a girlfriend?" she looked up at him.

He nodded. "Does it bother you?"

She smiled. "No. But I can see you're not happy with her like you are with me."

"Why you say that?"

"I can't tell you." She giggled. "It's a girl thang."

"Uh, you never told me your age."

"Too late for that, don't you think?" She smirked, lowering the soapy rag to his dick. "But no need to worry. I'm legal baby. FYI, I'll be twenty-one in August."

"Damn! You ain't even old enough to drink beer."

"True. But I'm old enough to drink you," she countered back, gently squeezing the rag around his dick.

His mind quickly jumped back to the early morning fuck he had with her. She sucked his dick twice, humming and licking him until he popped off in her mouth.

"I didn't think you would like me," Kahneko admitted as she caressed his balls.

"Why?"

She looked down at his flesh growing from her touch. "Because I'm small. I don't have no big boobs and a fat butt."

85

Lorenzo wanted to assure her that she was desirable in his eyes. "Half of them women you see on TV are fake."

"You think I'm sexy?" she asked affectionately.

"Fuck yeah!" Lorenzo palmed her cute little ass. "You got me wanting to slide up in the pussy right now.

"Anytime baby. I know how to play my position if you want to rock like that." She smiled. "And FYI, I know it's too late to change what we did. But I'm on the pill and I like doing it raw with you."

"Turn around for me." He rubbed her smooth ass. "I need some more of this pussy."

Kahneko didn't hesitate for a second to do as she was told. A shiver ran up her legs as Lorenzo bent her at the waist. Gripping her by the shoulders, he waited until she blindly reached back to guide him inside her. With the water pelting their nude flesh, he stroked her tight pussy with unhurried incessant strokes. Her face went slack with pleasure.

"Fuck me, Lorenzo. Make me cum again. Ohhh... yes!" she moaned as her ass smacked against him.

Lorenzo threw his head back as a wave of pleasure pushed up from his feet to his balls. He palmed her small tits, rocking himself in and out of her hot slit. With no thoughts of tomorrow, he stayed inserted in Kahneko, releasing his climax until he was spent.

***

"Feeling better, bruh?" Travis asked Lorenzo after Mikki and Kahneko left.

"I'm straight," Lorenzo replied as he dealt with regret and guilt over his actions with Kahneko. As much as that stood true, Lorenzo had exchanged numbers with Kahneko with a promise of a future hookup.

"Turn that digital scale on." Travis dumped a third pound bag of loose tobacco on the kitchen table. "Time to get down to the nitty-gritty of hustling behind bars."

"How much all this cost?" Lorenzo asked as Travis got up from the table to close the blinds in the living room.

"Forty-five dollars."

"For all three bags?"

"Yep," Travis answered from the living room. "Each bag is sixteen O's and outta that Mac can make thirty-two bricks."

"And how does that breakdown?"

"Each brick is twenty-eight grams in weight," Travis explained taking his seat back at the table. "G'head and weight it out on the scale."

Lorenzo pinched off a small amount of the fresh stringy tobacco then placed it on the pad of the digital scale.

"Put a little bit more. I can just about eyeball it and tell you that ain't twenty-eight grams."

Lorenzo nodded because the digital screen showed 19.50 grams. Adding more tobacco, Lorenzo looked up at Travis when the screen showed 28 grams.

"How much you think that's worth in prison?" Travis asked.

"Shit...ten bucks."

"Hell no. That's a fifty dollar brick all day long."

Lorenzo quickly did the math in his head. A pound had 16 O's, that's 32 bricks at $50 a pop...$1,600. Three pounds jumped the value to $4,800.

"So...you mean to tell me that you paid forty-five dollars and you'll make forty-eight hundred?"

"All day every day," Travis replied.

"I still don't see how or why an inmate will drop fifty for it."

"Here, I'll show you," Travis removed a tube of ChapStick from his pocket.

Lorenzo watched with interest as Travis filled the small white cap with tobacco.

"Behind bars," Travis dumped the tobacco out of the cap. "This is a phat roll-up that sells for two dollars and out of each brick you can get sixty roll-ups, so—"

"Uh, that's a hundred and twenty dollars."

"Bingo!" Travis smiled. "Now you see how the hustle don't stop. I got Mac on the inside selling nothing but bricks, but on his own he sells roll-ups. Mac hasn't clicked his own canteen card in over five months."

"So, Mac is a kingpin behind bars?"

"No," Travis pointed at himself. "That would be me."

"Okay. So when will you move all this shit?"

"Next week, and after that, I got two more orders for four more pounds."

Lorenzo did the math in his head again. The drop with the two phones $500, the three pounds on the table $4,800, and the four pounds next in line, $6,400. In less than two weeks at the max, Travis could hustle up $11,700.

Travis saw the disbelief written on Lorenzo's face. For that reason, he made up his mind to ease Lorenzo inside his hustle one step at a time. He figured Lorenzo wasn't ready to learn about the value of powder or a gram of coke behind bars.

"How about weed?" Lorenzo wanted to know. "How much is a cap worth?"

"Ten dollars."

"Damn! So that's…Six hundred dollars that can be made off twenty-eight grams of smoke!"

"Yeah. And if it's that Cush, dude gon' sell their soul."

"Ai'ight. I see how the value jumps up. But you still haven't told me how you're moving all this shit in. How in the hell do you get the phones through the metal detector we gotta walk through?"

"That's one thing you don't have to worry about and you gotta trust me on that."

Lorenzo hid his mood of being left in the dark on the subject. Shifting on the chair he stared at the mound of tobacco, running its prison value through his mind again. $1,600 for a $15 dollar bag.

"I got everything running smoothly," Travis broke Lorenzo's thoughts. "I got the market on the tobacco on lock. Mac is running it like I asked him to."

"And nobody hasn't tried to steal his shine?"

"The gangs keep the peace. Each group has a hustle that they cop through Mac. Example, the such-and-such crew can cop uh… say five caps of powder coke for two hundred. That's a good flip since they can make two hundred off each cap. So…eight hundred for two is good."

"I get it. Mac moves all the bricks of tobacco on the yard."

"And the phones?"

"So the weed, powder and coke… he sells it by weight to let the others make a flip."

"Correct. And that's the hustle but you ain't seen shit yet," Travis stood and smiled at Lorenzo. "I got a power move, bruh and I'm not gonna tell you no bullshit."

"Okay, what's up?"

"You saw what I got in my closet right. Well... what if I told you we can make double that amount in six months. Would you be down?"

Lorenzo thought back to the suitcase packed with $56,000 and the two others in the closet for a total of $168,000. With Travis speaking of doubling that amount, $336,000 easily took a grip of Lorenzo's attention.

Diving head first with money on his mind, Lorenzo told Travis to lay out the game that could put him on his feet with as less risk as possible.

Chapter Nine

Selma, North Carolina

Shayla tossed the last of Lorenzo's clothes inside the trash bag then yanked the plastic yellow drawstrings to close it. She cleared the sheen of sweat off her forehead with her palm. Four trash bags sat at her feet and yet she still searched for anything else that belonged to Lorenzo. Snapping her fingers, she rushed into the bathroom and snatched his toothbrush out of the chrome holder. She wanted everything of his out of her place, including his ass. Next, she dragged the trash bags one by one to the front porch, still pissed the fuck off behind Lorenzo's cheating ass. Her mood was beyond ill. Pure shock had seized her when that bitch had answered his phone. Shayla's vulnerability was weak when it came to rejection. Lorenzo, in her mind, had started some bullshit just so he could go and lay up with another bitch. Tears came easily at first, but now all Shayla had for her baby daddy was hate.

At the kitchen table, she sat with a pen and pad. This last token would show Lorenzo that Shayla was the wrong one to fuck with.

Dear Dummy

Since you can't answer my calls I see now that we don't have nothing to talk about! I don't care about that bitch you was laid up with, she can have your sorry ass! Here's all your shit so you have no reason to be up under my roof! As for our son, I will never break that bond, but for you and I, nigga I'm done with you. I TRIED to tell you what was up about that bikini but you ran off on me and your son! P.S. Your money is included with your shit. I don't need nothing from you. I can and will make it on my own.

She read the note twice before sliding back from the table. She knew he had to come home to get his uniform for work tomorrow. Her mom picked up Alonso two hours ago, but Shayla hadn't told her what was going on. By 5:30 p. m., Shayla was dressed and out the front door. She wasn't ready to face Lorenzo just yet. The first place he would look for her would be at her mom's.

Behind the wheel of her gray Altima, she fought back a new batch of tears that formed in her greenish-brown eyes. Her intentions were to just ride around to clear her mind until she rode pass the Rhodes Strip Club near I-95. Michelle jumped into her thoughts. Using the Bluetooth, she placed a call to Michelle while turning into the gas station.

"Hello?" Michelle's downtrodden voice sounded inside the car.

"Hey, girl. It's Shayla, did I wake you up?"

"Oh, hey, Shayla!" Michelle perked up. "No, I was just... just going through some mess right now, but I'm glad you called. What up with you?"

"Needing to clear my mind," Shayla replied.

"Wanna catch a movie?"

"Which one?"

"Um, how about a scary movie?" Michelle suggested.

"Cool. But since it's your idea. You gotta buy the tickets!" Shayla smiled for the first time since Lorenzo had left.

"Whatever," Michelle laughed.

The two agreed to hang out for the rest of the night. Michelle gave Shayla the directions to her townhouse in Goldsboro, then told her to drive safely.

Shayla had every intention to get over Lorenzo and move on with her life. The thoughts of being a single mother placed a small ball of worry in her stomach. But on the subject of Lorenzo, her thoughts were firm and direct. Fuck Lorenzo!

***

"You got to be fucking kidding me!" Lorenzo stared in disbelief at the note Shayla had written. He glanced at the trash bags, shaking his head. Pulling himself together, he pulled out the house key to take his shit back inside. To his surprise, the key didn't fit.

"Bullshit!" Lorenzo kicked the door. He called Shayla. After the second ring, his call went to voicemail. "Yo, Shayla! So you wanna play games? I got your letter and... fuck it!" He ended the call feeling like shit. *How in the fuck did she know I was with another girl!* Nothing made any sense to Lorenzo. Glancing at his watch, he saw it was five minutes to nine.

"Fuck!" he muttered, kicking one of the trash bags. Lorenzo turned toward the street and watched a cab rolling up the street with its headlights on. For a second, he thought about sitting in his car and waiting for Shayla to return. With his shoulders slumped, he grabbed the trash bags to leave. A part of him wanted to stay to make things right with Shayla but his ego stood in the way. He tossed the four bags in the back seat and slammed the door.

He slid behind the wheel and he stared at the apartment, wondering if it was really the end of his five-year relationship with Shayla. As he started his car up, he reluctantly called Travis before backing out of the driveway.

"Yo, what up?" Travis answered with loud music thumping in the background.

"Man, you won't believe what happened."

"What, you hit the lotto?"

"Nah, Shayla kicked me out."

"Word?"

"And she changed the fucking locks and left all my shit in some trash bags on the porch."

"What the fuck happened?"

Lorenzo shook his head. "Shit is crazy for real. Look. Where you at right now?"

"Heading back to the crib. Had to go and dig Lisa's back out with her freaky ass."

Lorenzo wasn't in the mood to hear any exploit's about cheating and being unfaithful. Being without Shayla and his son was a feeling he couldn't get content with.

"You gonna be able to make it to work tomorrow night?" Travis asked.

"I'm not sure right now, bruh. I can't even think straight right now as it is."

"Well, if you ain't got no place to go, you know you can crash at my crib until you and Shayla get things straight."

"Thanks, man, I'm on my way now."

Lorenzo backed out of the driveway with his issue weighing hard on his shoulders. If he could correct his wrong, he would have given Shayla the chance to speak instead of running off like he did.

Every idea that filled his mind about the green bikini ran on some grimy shit! When and where had she worn the bikini and for whom caused his thoughts to twist. Whatever the truth was, he realized he had a much bigger issue to deal with since

Shayla knew about Kahneko. As it filled his mind he wondered if Travis went behind his back to tell Shayla about Kahneko?

***

An hour later in Goldsboro, Shayla sat in Michelle's living room talking to her mom on the phone. To her surprise, her mom told her that she hadn't heard from Lorenzo.

"Is something going on with you two?"

"Uh, not right now, Mom. I mean, yes there's an issue, but I promise to tell you about it tomorrow when I pick Alonso up."

"He didn't hit you did he? Now you know I won't go for that."

"No mom, he didn't hit me okay."

"Well, just talk to me tomorrow. I love you."

"Love you too, mom, bye bye," Shayla hung up the phone just as Michelle came down the stairs.

"The kids are asleep," Michelle said having changed into a fitted tanktop and a pair of shorts. The two had viewed the movie and gave it high reviews from start to end.

"I really needed to get outta the house," Shayla let her emotions show a little.

"Me too," Michelle added but had no plans of telling Shayla about her issue.

"So… you really enjoy stripping?" Shayla asked.

Michelle playfully rolled her eyes. "I wouldn't use the word enjoy… but it's okay. It's not like I was forced to strip for money. I… just like all the attention I get from men to keep it real with you."

"You plan on making a career out of it?"

"Want me to be honest?" Michelle smiled.

"Nah. Tell a lie."

They both laughed.

Michelle stood then walked around the center living room table toward a DVD rack near the flat screen TV. "I'm hoping to use my stripping as a launching pad to something bigger."

"Like what?" Shayla asked as Michelle removed a DVD from the top of the tower-like rack.

"Porn." Michelle turned with the DVD.

"Porn! As in… like doing it in front of a bunch of people? Girl you are out of your mind." Shayla frowned.

Michelle took a seat back on the sofa. "Porn is where the real fame and money is." She handed Shayla the DVD. "You watch porn?"

"Sure," Shayla replied. "But doing it is not up my alley. Hell, I can hardly open my eyes just to strip."

"I think I can be a porn star." Michelle sounded confident of her aspiring goal.

"Are you serious?" Shayla checked out the cover art on the DVD.

"I sent my pictures to a porn company down in Miami," Michelle told her.

"This one?" Shayla held up the DVD. "Amatory Erotic Films?"

"Yep, and I'm really serious about doing it."

"Michelle, you're a pretty girl and I'm sure you know that. You don't have a problem with men, and we saw that tonight by those guys that tried to holler at you. I... just don't see why you would want to do something like this."

"I got my reason," Michelle murmured in a soft tone.

"Reason or reasons?"

"Both, I guess" Michelle shrugged. "I have two kids to support and I want the best for both of them. Yeah. I keep 'em in nice clothes and stuff, but my main goal is their future. When they turn twenty-one I want to be able to give them a jump on life. And I seriously don't want my girl to follow in my path. My kids' future is my reason."

Shayla flipped the DVD over to check out the dude on the cover. She found the brother deeply attractive.

"That's Trevon Harrison," Michelle grinned. "Have you seen him in action before?"

Shayla shook her head. "But I assume you have."

"Damn straight. I have all ten of his DVDs, and he's the main reason I wanna get put down with AEF."

"Why?"

"Because he only does porn with AEF exclusively and like I just said… you need to see him work it for yourself." Michelle blushed from her lewd thoughts of Trevon.

"Who's this big butt girl looking like Nicki Minaj beside him?" Shayla tapped the DVD with her pink fingernail.

"That's Kandi and she has a baby by him."

"And they're both still doing porn!"

"Nah. Kandi retired when she got pregnant, but Trevon is still in the biz slanging that sweet meat."

"That's crazy!"

"No, it's business."

"Okay, you said you sent some pictures. What's the next step?"

"Well." Michelle paused to clear her throat. "If they like what they see, they'll ask me to come down to Miami to do an audition to see how I can act in front of a camera."

"In other words, you'll go down there to get fucked," Shayla stated without biting her words.

Michelle nodded. "It's what I want to do, so I'm really hoping to get a call from them, soon."

Shayla laid the DVD on the arm of the sofa then reached for her purse off the floor. "Do you have a man?" Shayla prepared to leave.

"Nope. How about you?"

Shayla slid the strap of her purse over her shoulder, then thought of Lorenzo. She missed him, and the reality was a fact that she couldn't ignore. "I'm single too, girl. You know how it is."

Michelle had an idea that caused her to giggle.

"And what is funny?" Shayla asked, standing at the end of the sofa.

"Uh, since you will be alone tonight, maybe you should take one of my DVDs to check out Trevon."

"You know what?" Shayla nodded. "That might not be a bad idea."

***

Shayla arrived back at her two-bedroom apartment a little after midnight. Seeing the trash bags were gone she couldn't help but think of Lorenzo's reaction when he came to the conclusion of being kicked out on his ass. Her mind was made up, she wouldn't answer the door if he happened to come back home tonight. If he wanted to act stupid, she'd act a fool right along with him.

After a quick shower, she came out of the bathroom and sat at the foot of her bed. Looking over her bare shoulder she felt a tingle stir between her thighs. It had been a few months since she last enjoyed the unique pleasure with her sex toys. The sight of the vibrator she nicknamed Mr. Tap Out had her ready and willing to tap out after reaching a nut. Tonight she would add a little something special to her self-pleasure. Reaching for the TV remote she wanted to see all the hype behind Mr. Trevon Harrison. Once the porno started, Shayla stood and pulled her shirt off, dropping it to the floor.

Wanting to get right into the action she sped the porno up a few frames until she saw some fucking.

"Ohhh damn," she moaned reaching up to lightly pinch her tiny round nipples. On the screen, she caught her first impression of Trevon and it was a sight that warmed her instantly. The screen was filled with his spit covered dick easing in and out of Kandi's red coated lips. Shayla slid two fingers in her mouth then pushed three between her legs. The porno had her full attention even as she later laid on the bed fingering herself to a climax. She got caught up in her fantasy by calling out Trevon's name with Mr. Tap Out buzzing against her clit.

When Trevon reached his climax in Kandi's mouth on the screen, Shayla stuck her tongue out… wishing she could be in Kandi's position. She watched the entire 60-minute film and got herself off three times, shamelessly chanting out Trevon's name.

Too weak to take another shower, she fell asleep with a soaked pussy and sore fingers. She planned to spend some of her stripper money on an AEF DVD featuring Trevon Harrison. A fact stood, she was a new fan and her pussy would agree.

***

"What the hell!" Shayla raced out of her bedroom toward the living room window after seeing a pair of headlights in the driveway. She knew it wasn't Lorenzo because the engine was too loud. Fresh from the shower, the thin purple blouse clung to her damp flesh, outlining her perky breasts and full nipples. Her mouth dropped when she saw a tow truck in front of her car. With no care for how she was dressed, she hurried outside to stop the repo man from taking her ride. "Wait! Wait! Wait!" she shouted, racing to the front of her Altima. The repo man turned his flashlight off and held up the repo order for Shayla's car. Shayla snatched it, knowing what was on it.

"You're two months behind on your payment," the repo man stated in a flat tone.

"Please don't take my car," she glanced at his name tag, "Eddie. I will have the money tomorrow. Please don't do this."

He shrugged. "It's not me. It's your bank that made the repo order. All I do is tow the cars and that's it. Whatever you owe is between you and the bank."

Shayla knew she would lose her car for good if it was towed. "Sir, please! I need my car to go to work and to take care of my son. I'll have the money tomorrow night. What will one more day hurt?" she pleaded, hoping he would show some understanding for her plight.

"Sorry," he shrugged. "Again, it's not me. It's—"

"The bank!" Shayla balled up the repo order and threw it at Eddie's feet. She expected him to get upset but to her surprise, she noticed how his eyes ogled her breasts. A breath later she realized she stood in front of a stranger, barefooted, without a bra or panties on. The thin blouse sat high above her knees, leaving little to imagine what was under it. Instead of making an attempt to cover herself she stood her ground. Without her car, she would face a serious struggle that could end up being too much to handle. For a split second, she wished she would have kept the $5,000 Lorenzo got from Travis. Wishing for anything past or future wasn't going to help Shayla tonight. Thinking of now and what she needed, she allowed Eddie to openly look at her breast.

"What if my car wasn't here tonight?" she asked as a light breeze blew the diesel fumes from the tow truck in her face.

Eddie shrugged again. "Guess I would come back another day. And if you were to make your payments within two days, the repo order would be canceled."

Shayla knew what she had to do. *Wait, I can't do this. Lorenzo has the money. I can call him and get it.* A second later her jaw tightened. *Fuck him! He's with another bitch and I can do fine without him!* Shayla acted off her anger and heartbreak with her next move. "I think we can help each other out, Eddie." Shayla fidgeted with the hem of the blouse.

"How?"

"Turn your truck off and follow me inside."

He shook his head. "Lady, I have a job to do and I can't let you distract me from doing my job."

"We can make a deal." Shayla pressed. "I saw how you looked at my breasts. Fuck the bank. I'll pay them soon but I can't let you take my car."

"A deal?"

Shayla nodded. "I'm on my period," she lied. "But I'll let you suck my nipples while I give you a hand job. All I need is one more day."

Eddie sighed. "Lady, if you're needing your car that bad—"

"I do," Shayla blurted, fighting back her tears.

Chapter Ten

Goldsboro, North Carolina
June 14th, Friday

"You're not making any sense," Brittney complained as she followed Michelle into her bedroom. "You've been looking for Rikeith's father since day one, and now that you've found him you're not taking out child support?"

"It was never about the money, Brittney," Michelle replied as she stood at the dresser removing her earrings.

"I don't understand it."

"You're too young, that's why."

Brittney stood at the edge of the bed with her arms crossed. "So you're just gonna let this guy be a deadbeat and not help you?" She wondered in disappointment.

"I don't need his help." Michelle turned. "He doesn't care about Rikeith, and I'm not about to put my son through any drama."

"I'd take his ass to court if I were you. Heck, I'd call Maury."

"Not gonna happen."

"Uh, how many times did you do it with this guy?"

Michelle sighed. "Just once, okay. It was a one-night stand and we had a little... accident."

Brittney frowned. "I still think you're wrong, but it's your life."

"Thanks for your advice, whether you believe me or not."

Brittney yawned, "I'm going back downstairs to check on the kids. Plus its time for Rikeith's nap."

Michelle had to admit that Brittney was mature for her young age. Today wasn't the first time Brittney had tried to steer Michelle from her wrong. When she was alone in her bedroom, she ran her fingers through her hair, flopping down on the bed. Her head hung toward the floor as she tried to convince herself that she made the right moves concerning Travis. Forcing him to be a part of Rikeith's life made no sense to her.

"I don't need his sorry ass!" Michelle muttered to herself as she packed her clothes for work tonight. As she turned out the lights in her bedroom, she got a text message from Shayla.

On my way out the door. See you @ work. TTYL

Michelle kissed her kids goodbye then told Brittney that she would text her when she got to work. At 9:30 p. m., she drove off in her Yukon with a new single by Iggy Azalea thumping from the speakers.

***

Friday nights were the busiest at Club Twerk It and the packed parking lot proved it. All eighteen strippers were on deck tonight to cater to the ballers, hustlers, and freaks, VIP stayed turnt up with friction bed dances that were deemed an upgrade from lap dances. Titties bounced free from bras and money rained around asses and glasses of bubbly.

Girls openly flirted for them colored dollars, blowing kisses and winking at any man that showed signs of parting ways with their money.

The music shook the walls with K. Camp while a wide hip stripper had her ass clapping to the beat on stage. Men in thuggish gear stood around the stage, locked in awe of the stripper's oily, jiggly ass. In darkened corners of the club, erections were gripped and rubbed for a twenty tucked inside a thong or G-string. The bar kept the drinks flowing while request was shouted out nonstop over the music. Strippers from thin to super thick mingled with the crowd, snagging lap dances or running game for a free drink. The security stayed tight, with their main concern centered around the strippers and their safety. They were on a constant patrol for the scent of weed. Anyone caught smoking weed was escorted out the door, and it didn't matter who they were nor how long their paper was. Those that were regular guests curbed the drama of being booted out by getting lifted *before* they came inside.

Jewelry sparkled in ears, belly buttons, around necks, belly chains, nose rings, around ankles, wrists, fingers, and even a few diamond coated teeth.

"I might as well be naked," Shayla commented on how the white thong exposed all of her ass.

"That's the point." Michelle reached for a tube of lip gloss from her makeup kit. "You should wear that baby tee instead of that bikini top. You'll show your nipple prints better."

Shayla untied the bikini as two strippers strolled into the dressing room. Both wore heavy makeup with long hair extensions flowing down their shoulders.

"How's business, Sinnamon?" Michelle asked the shorter of the two strippers.

"It's okay. But I heard it's popping off up in VIP," Sinnamon replied sliding out the chair at her dressing booth. "You must be the new girl?" Sinnamon glanced at Shayla.

"Sinnamon, meet my girl, Monàe," Michelle introduced the two, also reminding Shayla to use her stripper name.

Shayla traded the bikini top for a white ripped baby tee that showed off her perky tits. She stood in front of the mirror, pleased with the sight. From the platform heels to the blue wig, Shayla could hardly recognize herself. Turning from the mirror, she watched Michelle gently rubbing baby oil over the contour of her left breast.

"Don't forget rule number one, Monàe." Creame commented after her transformation was complete.

"I won't, Creame." Monàe smiled. "Don't give out my real name."

Creame and Monàe exited the dressing room together. Monàe couldn't hide her wide-eyed expression as she hit the floor with Creame.

"Just smile and follow me," Creame shouted above the pounding music and cheers from the stage. "And don't snap on anybody that grabs your ass."

"Will I have to hit the stage tonight?" Monàe asked as they headed toward the bar.

"I doubt it," Creame looked over her shoulder. "Do you want to?"

"Nah. Not yet."

Creame rocked her 47 inches of hips and ass with each step. Tonight she wore a pair of blueish see-thru platform heels and a black fishnet bodysuit with a thong. Her 36D's were out for all eyes to see with only a gold star-shaped pasties over each nipple. Breezing by a table of three men, she was stopped.

"Yo, Creame!" one of the men shouted. "Lemme holla at chu right quick."

Creame winked at Monàe. "Hold on a sec."

Monàe stood beside a tower of speakers as Creame sauntered toward the table. She watched Creame lean over the table to talk to the dude that called her. While she chatted, the guy to her right reached out and rubbed Creame's ass. Monàe took note how Creame didn't flinch, nor did she push the hand away.

"Hey, sexy."

Monàe flinched at the sudden presence that snuck up behind her. She spun, just as a pair of hands came to rest on her tiny waist. Her first reaction was the flip all the way out. But not tonight, she was at work. All emotions of tripping or going off were replaced with lust. The dude standing over her and all up on her ass was a dead ringer for Chris Brown, only he was darker and rocked gold teeth. Monàe managed a smile.

"You must be new. What's your name?"

"I can hardly hear you." Monàe pointed at her ear. "Let's go over to the bar."

Monàe escorted her first client by the hand through the packed club. It excited her and lifted her self-esteem that someone had found her natural petite frame sexy. Reaching the bar, she couldn't hide her grin. A tingle ran up her legs when he helped her get up on the stool.

"Damn! You fine as hell, ma. So what's yo handle?" he asked again and all up in her personal space.

"My handle?" Monàe frowned.

"Your name," he told her as he leaned against the bar top.

She smiled shyly. "Monàe," she told him, hoping her wig was on straight.

He nodded, never taking his eyes away from hers. "This your first night?"

"Yes," she replied as the scent of his cologne tickled her nose. Monàe figured he was a regular visitor for him to pick out that she was new.

"I didn't mean to scare you when I walked up on ya," he said, reaching for her hand.

"It's okay." She shrugged. *Damn this nucca is fine!*

"Have you been on stage yet?"

"Not yet."

"Hmmm…have you given anyone a lap dance?"

She shook her head and tried to stay calm when his eyes fell to her prominent nipple prints.

"You ain't nothing but a baby doll." He licked his lips. "So what I gotta do to be your first lap dance?"

Monàe stared at his sexy lips as his free hand slid up her bare thigh. She sat motionless, surprised that she enjoyed his touch.

"Can you find a table?" Monàe broke the trance.

"I don't do the tables, baby." He squeezed her hip. "Ain't nothing but VIP for me, or we can go someplace else."

"Let's stick with the VIP." She smiled.

"C'mon then." He lifted her light frame off the stool and down to the floor.

Across the club, Creame wiggled her way through the crowded floor searching for Monàe. She scanned the dimly lit club for Monàe's blue wig near the stage and the bar. Creame began to worry. She didn't think Monàe was ready to work the floor on her own. There were too many dangers Monàe wasn't aware of, and Creame could confirm all of them. Before she reached the bar, a loud round of shouts and applause exploded behind her near the stage. Turning at the waist, she saw the cause of the excitement. Sinnamon was on all fours wearing black padded knee pads and twerking hard against a dildo that was fitted on the pole. The entire club had a side view of the dildo easing in and out of Sinnamon's phat pussy. She controlled the crowd, earning a shower of money raining all around her explicit sex act. Each time she made the ten-inch dildo disappear between her legs, it only drove the crowd closer to losing control. Creame knew Sinnamon wouldn't stop fucking the dildo until she climaxed. Since the sight wasn't new to Creame, she turned her focus back to finding Monàe. Stepping around a table of two men and a stripper sitting between them, Creame suddenly froze. Her eyes went across the club toward the stairs that headed up to VIP. She spotted Monàe going upstairs with a face that was known to her. He was all up on Monàe, talking in her ear with one hand caressing her ass. Creame narrowed her eyes. Her temper quickly heated.

"Creame." Shaun appeared in front of Creame, seemingly out of thin air.

Creame blinked, taking a small step backward. Whatever Shaun had to say, Creame hoped she would be quick about it. Shifting her gaze from Monàe disappearing up in VIP to Shaun, Creame sensed something was wrong. Shaun grilled her hard.

"Is there something wro—"

"I need to speak to you in my office!" Shaun stated. "Now!"

Creame acted like everything was cool as she followed Shaun to her office. A few strippers glanced at Creame, but quickly looked away which only added to Creame's worry.

Her platform heels clacked against the uncarpeted hallway floor that led to Shaun's office. Creame had never shown any disrespect to see the flip side of Shaun's emotions so tonight she didn't know how to react. She assumed it would be something minor. Something like Shaun being upset over a late check-in. All of Creame's minor reasons were crushed when she saw Sayveon sitting in the office with his shoulders slumped.

Shaun slammed the door and pointed at Creame to sit her ass down. Not a word broke the tense silence until Shaun sat down behind her desk.

"How long have you been working here, Creame?" Shaun asked.

"Almost a year," Creame replied.

Shaun nodded. "And by now you should know I'm fair and I treat everyone with respect. With that being true, I don't show no mercy when anyone takes my kindness for a weakness." Shaun picked up her iPhone. "So how long have you been doing it?"

"Doing what?" Creame asked as her stomach turned. *This can't be anything good.*

"Tricking up in VIP!" Shaun snapped.

Creame gasped, glancing at Sayveon and thinking he had ratted her out. She was speechless but quickly began to form a lie to save her job. *Shit! It's his word against mine. I'll just say he's mad because I won't give him no pussy and turn it back on his—*

"This video was sent to my phone last night!" Shaun held her iPhone toward Creame with the volume up loud. The footage showed one of the VIP private booths with its black velour curtains shut. The faint sound of moans and flesh smacking came from the speaker. Whoever filmed the scene had quietly snuck up to the VIP booth and parted the curtains. Creame sank low in the chair when she saw herself on the screen with Derrick long stroking her from the back.

"Clear all of your shit out of the dressing room!" Shaun stated. "And Sayveon will escort you to your ride."

"Please, Shaun, I—"

"I don't wanna hear it, Creame. You're fired!" Shaun told her firmly. "I hired you to be a dancer. Not a damn prostitute!"

115

Chapter Eleven

Maury Correctional Institution

July 15th Saturday

"Attention on the institution, code two count is clear, code two count is clear."

Mac rolled off his bunk at 12:10 a. m. in his darkened cell in A-block. Like every other weekend, the dayroom stayed open up until midnight instead of 11:00 p. m. on the weekdays. While everyone else was locked back until breakfast, it was time for Mac to go to work. He brushed his teeth, then threw on a fresh gray tee and a pair of DPS-issued pants. His outfit stayed the same, 365 days a year. He pressed the call button and his cell door slid open eight seconds later at 12:15 a. m.

"Yo, Mac! Who in the booth?"

Mac recognized the voice of Scar Murda, a high-ranking gang member that slept downstairs. "It looks like Ms. Hart," Mac replied, his voice slightly echoing in the empty and quiet dayroom.

"Tell 'er phat ass she need tah come up outta that booth and make some rounds!" Scar Murda joked.

Mac laughed. "Ain't fuckin' with her crazy ass!"

"Mac!" A second inmate by the name of NaNa shouted when Mac reached the bottom of the stairs.

"Yeah, what up?"

"Tell that stupid bitch Hart ta bust my door! I done hit the call button a hundred damn times!"

"I gotcha," Mac replied just as NaNa's door slid open.

"'Bout fuckin' time!" NaNa yelled as he stepped out of his cell without a shirt on. A second later, a second door popped open three cells down from NaNa.

"Hey, Mac, try to bring some small trash bags," the second dorm janitor Nate said from within his cell.

"How many?" Mac asked.

Nate came to his door. "Four if you can."

"I gotcha," Mac said just as CO Hart opened the dorm slider so he could leave the block. As usual, NaNa and Nate began to playfully argue about who would have to clean the up and downstairs showers. Mac was anxious to see Sergeant Parker. Whatever bond she wanted, he knew the next move would be made by her.

When Mac reached the main hallway he nodded at Hart up in the booth then stopped at the sergeant's office. The door was wide open and Sergeant Parker sat alone at the desk.

"Hey, Mac," Parker glanced up from the flat screen monitor. "Good news. I got all the supplies from the warehouse."

"Ai'ight. I'll sweep the hall first then mop and wax."

She nodded. "Come in for a second and close the door."

Mac kicked the door stopper up, then took a seat in front of her desk. His mind jumped immediately back to their last encounter in A-Block. *Bet she gonna talk about seeing me naked.*

"You're different." She twirled an ink pen in her left hand.

Mac shifted in the chair. "Different how?"

"You don't follow the norm," Parker answered. "More than half of the men on this unit are in a gang."

Mac shrugged. "I wasn't born in that lifestyle."

She nodded. "Also, I never heard any reports from my female staff about you... um, exposing yourself in the shower nor in your cell."

"I don't get down like that, but every man to his own."

"Did anyone believe what happened the last time I saw you?" Her face turned red as a smile tugged the corners of her lips.

"I keep my business to myself."

"So, you told no one?"

"Nope. Did you?"

Sergeant Parker laughed briefly, then laid the pen down. "Well, in that case." She smiled at him. "I liked what I saw and I really mean that."

Mac knew at that very moment he had to shuffle the cards in his favor. "Anything that goes down between us stays between us."

She nodded. "But let's face reality, Mac. I know I wouldn't be your type if you were free and met me on the street."

"What's reality?" he questioned, unconcerned of how she looked. "What's important is the way your mere... presence affected me."

"Mmm, that was a nice *affect* to look at. Um, what did you do after I left?"

Mac stared at her. "I thought of you and took care of my personal business," he lied.

Sergeant Parker blushed. "You really jacked off and thought about me?"

"Ain't no shame in it." *Damn! She turning me on!*

"Did you cum?"

He nodded. *Man, she is bugging for real.*

"Do you want to be my secret?"

Mac saw the seriousness in her eyes. "That sounds like a good idea."

She smiled. "Good. And FYI, I don't want to hear about you being a secret with anyone else. I want all of you to be for my eyes and pleasure only." *There. I said it.*

"You won't have to ever worry 'bout that," Mac replied with what she wanted to hear.

Sergeant Parker picked the pen back up and stared at Mac lustfully. "I'll talk to you later."

Mac stood and just as he was willing to bet, her gaze dropped to his dick print. The pen twirled faster in her pale fingers.

"Before I go," he stated, "I hope I'm the only guy you're dealing with in my position. Real talk, ain't tryna be looking over my shoulder for any other secret friends you might have. If it's gonna be us, then that's it."

Sergeant Parker looked up at Mac. "I'm not that stupid, okay? Besides, I have a strong feeling that you're all the man I need."

"That's what up because in here I want to be your one and only secret."

"I'm married." She informed him.

"I have no control over that, but I'll deal with it."

Silence. A second later, Sergeant Parker nodded at the door.

"Open it back up and be sure to stop by to see me before you go back to the block."

"Ai'ight. I'll talk to you later."

Mac eased out of the office then headed to the storage room. His mind ran a million miles a second. Bagging a female CO was a rare occurrence for Mac to deal with. It took a rare breed of man to stand apart from the norm to gain the attention of a female CO. Being that Parker was a sergeant had Mac on a different level. Behind bars, the game of flirting had no comparison to the free world. Women that received little or no attention from men on the street are treated to a life altering phase when they become a CO. From day one, men are constantly in their face, flirting and vying for their attention. Mac understood the game. He realized that any female CO, regardless of how she looked or how old she was, could be with *any* man behind bars to her picking. Mac knew his role and position. But fucking with Sergeant Parker he would have to understand her motive and find out why she was suddenly swinging from his dick. Like most cases in relationships between an inmate and staff, there was a need and a want seeded on both sides. Mac would have to find out both in Parker's motive. What the fuck did she want?

***

Dixon, Watson, and Hart were kicking it in the staff break room when Mac tapped on the door. Hart paused her fresh gossip to get up to open the door.

"Come to empty the trash," Mac lifted up a new large trash bag in his hand.

Dixon casually rubbed his chin, then turned his attention back to the newspaper. Beside him, Watson had his head down picking at his food.

"You waxing the floor tonight?" Hart asked as Mac took out the heavy bag of trash.

"Yeah."

"Well, let me know before you start, so I can carry my ass back up in the booth."

"For what? So you can go to sleep?" Mac chuckled.

"Somebody done told you wrong if I won't," she laughed.

Mac stole a long look at Hart's plump ass when she turned to reach for her radio. *Mmm! I know that pussy some fire!* He lusted over her. In Mac's sight, Hart was the Queen Bee on Blue Unit. Her hair and nails stayed done and her ass and titties went on pass tomorrow and well into next week. She didn't seek much attention from inmates, so the less in her face the better.

"Can you clean out the microwave later on?" Hart asked as Mac tied the trash bag in a knot.

"Yeah, I'll get around to it before I go in."

A minute later, Mac was in the storage room with the door shut. He moved quickly, ripping the trash bag open to search for Dixon's drop. The search ended when Mac found a box of KFC chicken wrapped inside a green plastic bag. Mac already knew the contents of the box. Three prepaid smartphones, eight caps worth of powdered coke, one memory card, one bottle of Polo cologne and a three piece snack of extra crispy fried chicken. Mac removed the KFC box from the trash bag and hid it in the second bag of ripped sheets and old towels. By the time another two minutes went by, Mac had the trash in a new trash bag. Everything was perfect and in order.

His next move would be the transportation of the package to his cell. He loaded the trash bag on the gray plastic two-level cart, placing it on the top. The clear bag with the sheets and towels went on the bottom. Mac pushed the cart out of the storage room, playing it cool and calm. He rolled the cart right pass the sergeant's office and through the first set of doors that led to his block. NaNa and Nate were still bullshitting about cleaning the dorm when Mac rolled the cart in. Mac's duties began with him collecting all the trash bags from all six dorms to be taken to the dumpster. Shooting the shit with Nate, Mac took the cloth bag up to his cell. Along the way he paused to collect any torn or ripped sheets and towels that some of the guys left outside of their cells. Mac would have to recycle the sheets and towels into rags that the dorm janitor and himself would use for cleaning. No one paid any attention when Mac slid inside his cell with the bag. Once inside he locked the door, then threw a blind up over the cell door window. Two of the cell phones would be delivered tonight. Everything else, the four caps of powder and one cell phone, would sit until tomorrow.

"Block 'bout to be wet! Police coming through making rounds!"

Mac heard NaNa shout a second before the main slider door clanked open. By saying the block was *wet*, it gave the block a heads up that a female was going to come through.

"Hart making rounds on the bottom high side!" NaNa warned the block.

"Shole is and y'all better put your dicks up because I don't want to see them. And don't act like your ass is sleeping with your dick all outcha boxers!" Hart shouted.

Mac didn't panic. The bottom high side was the row of cells below him numbered 45 to 25 in odd numbers. The bottom low side were cells 1 to 23 in odd numbers. The top low were cells 2 to 24 in even numbers followed by the top high cells 26 to 48 in even numbers.

"Hart coming round the bottom low side!" NaNa called out Hart's new position. A few seconds later, Mac heard her coming up the stairs. "Hart going up on the top low. Block wet!"

"I gotcha wet!" Hart shouted at NaNa. "You need to hurry up and clean this funky block!"

Mac left his blind up while he finished his business. He tucked the cell phones back inside the sheets and towels bag, then flushed the toilet when he heard Hart near his cell.

"You alive in there?" Hart tapped on his door.

"Yeah. Using the toilet." *Why couldn't it have been Hart on my dick instead of Parker?*

"Okay. Just take the blind down when you're done."

Mac waited until NaNa announced the block was clear before he pressed the call button. Stepping out of his cell, he went back to work by collecting all the sheets and towels in A-block. He did nothing out of the norm to draw any attention to himself. Being on point was a must to make it day by day behind bars. Not only did Mac have to stay ahead of the prison staff, inmates were snitching as if it were a new fad. Envy and hate ran high in prison. Honor was fiction and respect was fantasy, but Mac knew how to maintain and keep the bullshit at arms distance. He placed himself above no man. Six minutes later he made it out of A-block, then hit B and C-block without any problems. The two cellphones had to be dropped off down in E-block, at the opposite end of the unit. The trip would take Mac back down the hall and pass the sergeant's office. Again, the door was wide open and Mac heard a loud, deep voice discussing something about TV staying on at count time. As Mac rolled the cart down the hall, the OIC (Officer In Charge), Lieutenant Stancil jumped from the chair, ending his conversation with Sergeant Parker. He stepped out into the hall and motioned for Mac to stop.

"What's up, lieutenant?" Mac slowed to a stop as the bald white OIC walked up on him. Behind the lieutenant, Sergeant Parker shrugged.

"Where are you coming from?" the lieutenant asked Mac.

"From C-block."

"Doing what?"

"He's the unit nighttime hall janitor," Parker hoped to ease the OIC back.

"Does he always move around unsupervised?"

"Sure," Parker replied.

The OIC stared at Mac, then took a step closer to examine the cart. Sgt. Parker exchanged a glance at Mac as if to say. *He's an ass. Just relax.* Relaxing was the last thing on Mac's mind. If he was caught with the two cell phones, it was an automatic six months on lockdown. The OIC stayed on some bullshit, and with rank, it gave him the power to fuck with inmates.

"I need two male staff." The OIC pulled out his cuffs. "I wanna strip-search this inmate right now."

Sergeant Parker rolled her eyes then pulled her radio from her hip to call Dixon and Watson.

Chapter Twelve

"How in the fuck did this happen?" Michelle shouted at Sayveon as he escorted her across the parking lot toward her Yukon. "Who sent that video?"

"I don't know," he replied with a shrug. "There were so many people in VIP that night."

Michelle blinked a pool of tears from her eyes. Stripping was her lifeline. It paid all the bills and kept food on the table for her kids and clothes on their backs.

"For all it's worth. I seriously tried to convince Shaun to let you stay."

Michelle lowered her chin when she reached her SUV. "I can't believe this is happening to me!"

Sayveon took some of the blame. He moved up behind her, placing his hands on her hips. "I really tried to help you, Creame."

"It's Michelle," she corrected him. "I'm out of a job, remember?"

"I shoulda never let you keep doing your thang."

"Then why did you? Oh, I know, 'cause I was sucking your—"

"No," he turned her around. "I know you have two mouths to feed, and I rather you do your hustle here where it is safe, you know."

She smiled. "Well, since you put it like that I won't be upset with you."

Sayveon stared at Michelle and admired her stunning looks. The skintight denim jeans caressed all of her soft curves. Being around her was a physical battle for Sayveon to stay true to his stance of not fucking a stripper. Showing pity for her, he dipped into his pocket and gave her a thick knot of cash. "It ain't much." He watched the black Toyota Avalon cruise by them.

"Thanks," she whispered.

"It ain't nothing. So I guess this is where we say goodbye."

Michelle hugged Sayveon, planting a pouty lip kiss on his cheek. He hugged her back, both hands dropping to her juicy ass for one more squeeze.

"For the record," she replied seductively. "I woulda kept sucking your dick even if I wasn't doing my thang up in VIP."

"Really?" He pulled her closer, pressing his erection against her body.

She nodded. "This ain't gotta be our goodbye."

"Shaun won't take you back in. Trust me on that."

"Fuck her. I'm talking about us. You and me." Michelle slid her tongue into his mouth before he could speak. She wasn't surprised when he kissed her back, squeezing her ass in a lustful attempt to mold it. In the heat of their lust, he backed her up against her ride, tonguing her down. She welcomed his aggressive kiss but the truth was, she welcomed the money. He showed a weakness and Michelle was showing her strength. Her emotions were ignored. Right now she stood heartless.

Sayveon broke from her sweet mouth, then lowered his lips to kiss the top of her cleavage.

"Just ask me," she offered. "All you have to do is ask."

"Ask you what?" He looked up.

Michelle gazed into his eyes. "For some pussy," she purred, reaching down to squeeze his erection. "I'm not a stripper no more."

He sighed. "I... can't, Creame... I mean Michelle. I'm married."

"So what!" she snapped shoving him back. "What difference does it make to put your dick in my mouth or pussy, huh?"

"I just can't." He backed up with his palms showing.

"Fuck you, okay!" Michelle was humiliated by his rejection. Through new tears, she turned away from him and jumped into her SUV. In her anger and regret, she forgot all about Shayla. Not once did she look back as she left Sayveon and the strip club behind.

***

Derrick continued his night with a third topless lap dance from Monàe inside the same VIP booth, where he smashed out Creame. Monàe found her zone, grinding on Derrick's lap with his mouth latched on her left nipple. He looked up at her. "That's it, baby." He blew against her wet nipple. "G'head and bust that nut!"

Monàe bit her bottom lip, grinding her body in a rhythm against Derrick's erection under his jeans.

"Get yours, baby." He nibbled on her left nipple then flicked it side to side with this tongue.

"Mmmmmm shit!" Monàe moaned as her hips twirled instinctively. "You got me so damn hot."

Derrick flicked his tongue lightly across her nipple, then tried to dip his fingers down the front of her thong. "Lemme make you cum," he murmured around her breast.

Monàe wanted to stop him, but at the moment, she wanted to cum. A twing of raw guilt filled her when Derrick's fingers brushed against her clit. She gasped, but leaned back to give his fingers full entrance to her damp pussy. She kept her eyes closed, then rode the warm waves of pleasure that moved between her legs. Soft moans danced off her glossy red lips as she fucked herself on his two fingers. His tongue circled her nipples, she felt as if she floated in thin air. With her arms circled his neck, she began to fantasize that the fingers inside her and the mouth latched to her nipple belonged to Lorenzo. Something clicked within her. She couldn't resist the sudden climax that grew between her thighs. Monàe didn't breathe until the five-second nut had loosened its grip. Derrick rubbed her breasts with his dick stretched tight under his jeans.

"I... have to go," she blurted.

"Hold up, baby." Derrick tried to keep her planted on his lap.

She jumped off his lap, embarrassed about the wet stain she left on his jeans. His words didn't slow her as she snatched up her top and $150 before pushing her way out of the booth. For the first time in four and a half years, another man had touched her sexually, whose name wasn't Lorenzo Watson. She felt so guilty having allowed another man to get her off.

Moments later, Monàe was back in the dressing room with six other strippers. She sat at Creame's booth wondering why it was empty. Beside her was a light-skinned stripper with oversized nipples pulling a pair of yellow and white thigh-highs up her slim legs. Her fake eyelashes were nearly half an inch long, giving her a comical look in Monàe's opinion.

"Um, excuse me. Have you seen Creame?" Monàe asked.

The topless stripper shook her head. "Nah. I'm just now getting here myself. Holler at La'Ashia."

"Who is she?"

"Last dressing booth to the back."

Monàe took the blue wig off then stood. "Thanks." She made her way to the back, sidestepping a heavyset stripper dancing in the middle of the room. Monàe assumed she was practicing some moves for the stage. Near the back, she walked up on a cute tatted up girl filing her nails at her dressing booth.

"Excuse me. Are you La'Ashia?"

La'Ashia lifted her hazel eyes to study Monàe in the mirror. After a seconds pause, she spun around on the stool. "You're the new girl, huh?"

Monàe nodded. "I'm Monàe."

"La'Ashia." She extended her hand. "What's up?"

"Um, have you seen Creame? Her booth is empty and—"

"So you haven't heard the bad news, huh?" La'Ashia was surprised. "Creame was shown the door tonight. She got fired."

"Fired! For what? Hell, she just got here!"

La'Ashia sighed. "You didn't hear it from me, but the word is that she got caught fucking for money up in VIP. Shaun found out and it was a wrap. Smoking green and tricking here is a no-no," La'Ashia said flatly.

"How long ago did this happen?"

"A couple of minutes before midnight."

Monàe thanked La'Ashia for the 411, then hurried back to Creame's dressing booth. *I don't believe any of this mess!* Monàe thought as she strolled through the list of numbers stored in her smartphone. Her first call went unanswered. She called a second time, hoping Michelle would pick up. Frustration was masked on her face as she elected to send a text message.

WTF! Where R.U? Did Shaun fire U? Call me ASAP!

Monàe suddenly felt alone without Creame. None of the other strippers paid her any mind. Monàe picked up the vibes that everyone looked out for themselves and she couldn't blame them. She stared at herself in the mirror. *Well, Shayla. Looks like the show must go on.* Monàe went to work on her *real* hair. *I don't need no funky ass wig!* she reasoned, seeing that her natural hair was longer and sexier than the wig. The baby tee and damp white thong were traded for a black bodysuit with circles up the sides. After she wiggled her ass inside the clinging suit, one of the strippers walked by and gave Monàe an approving nod. La'Ashia added her viewpoint by telling everyone that Monàe had a sexy shape just like Rihanna.

Monàe later strutted out of the dressing room and back on the floor. She was stopped instantly the second her gold and black stiletto heels hit the tiled black flooring. A heavyset guy whispered in her ear asking for a bed friction dance.

"You mean, a friction bed dance," she corrected him.

"Yeah, my bad. So what it do?" he asked with a crooked grin, "I got that money, baby."

"How ya money looking?" she flirted against her will. Her bills were her motive.

"Jeremy! What up, my dude!" Derrick appeared and slapped the big dude on the shoulder. "I see you met my number one stunna, Monàe."

Jeremy took a meek step back, dropping his meaty palms from Monàe's hips. "Yeah... um, was just askin' her if she had any homegirls to plug me in with."

Derrick slid his arm possessively around Monàe's waist, then turned his back on Jeremy.

"That was rude!" Monàe frowned, crossing her arms. "I do have a job."

"You're mine as long as I'm here." He grinned and then removed a Big Mac wad of money from his pocket. "Two stacks right here and all you gotta do to earn it is hang wit' me for the rest of the night."

Monàe shifted to a sexy bowlegged stance in the heels. *Who is this dude?* She eyed the money, noticing that most of the folded bills were twenties or fifties. Again, she clicked with an instant attraction toward him. Under the red and green strobe lights, she took in his handsome features.

"You... changed clothes." She observed the fresh all-white Marc Ecko outfit that draped over his masculine frame.

"Had to." He smiled, exposing his bottom row of gold teeth. "You left all that sweet juice on my jeans."

She covered her mouth and giggled. "Um, sorry about that."

"Shit, next time I hope you do it on my face."

"You're nasty."

"And you're sexy as hell. Too sexy for me to share you."

Monàe's attention moved to a thick, rose gold chain around his neck. At the end of it hung an icey medallion. "What does PBH stand for?"

"Stop frontin' yo." He chuckled. "I know you know what it means."

"Wrong. I have no idea."

Derrick rubbed his chin. "Where you from?"

"Nope. I don't get personal."

"Oh, it's like that?" he said, feeling up to the game of chasing her. "Ai'ight, I can respect that. But this chain." He tapped the pricey medallion. "It's my crew. Pretty Boy Hustlerz."

Monàe rolled her eyes. "And I'm supposed to be in awe of that?"

"So you gonna judge me?"

"No."

Derrick licked his lips, pressing for what he wanted. "Let's dead the bullshit. I just wanna rock wit' you for tonight. The bread is yours up front. All I wanna do is be around you, so what's up?"

"Why me?" she asked. "There are a bunch of other girls up in here with bigger butts and—"

"Whoa, baby. Ain't no shallow ass dude when it comes to seeing a true woman. Ain't even pressed to spend a penny on some of these ratchet crumb snatchers. I just see something different in you."

Monàe wasn't easily convinced with his words. *Okay... he's fine and got money. If he's dumb enough to hit me off with two grand, I'll be smart enough to take it.* "Can you buy me a drink?" she purred flirtatiously leaning closer.

Derrick tilted her chin up and met her stare. "Fuck around and flip your cards right and I'll buy yo' ass the club," he bragged.

Monàe was oblivious to the hateful look that followed her across the club and up the stairs to VIP. In one night, Monàe had gained a new enemy amongst a crowd full of strangers.

Chapter Thirteen

Maury Correctional Institution 12:50 a. m.

Mac held his boiling anger in check while he was strip-searched by the OIC, Watson, and Dixon. Being subjugated to the bullshit strip-search was a part of prison life Mac could never get accustomed to. Dixon and Watson had to follow the orders given by the OIC who stood by the door in the storage room.

"Check that bag on the bottom." The OIC nodded at Watson as Dixon stood beside Mac. "And look under the cart too."

Mac balled up his fist with the cuffs back around his wrist. *Hate these fucking cuffs!*

"You mad about something?" Lieutenant Stancil got up in Mac's face.

"Nah, I'm good," Mac forced his words, knowing Stancil wanted a reason to lock his ass up.

"You STG? Which group you with?" Lieutenant Stancil tilted his head. "Crip, Blood, Folk… I know you down with one of 'em." STG stood for Security Threat Group.

"I stand on my own," Mac replied as Watson dumped the bag of sheets and towels on the floor behind the OIC.

"You're mad over this strip-search?" Stancil wanted to provoke Mac to lash out so he could send him to segregation.

"Y'all just doing your job like I'm doing my time," Mac replied, without meeting Lieutenant Stancil's stare. He could smell Stancil's peppermint scented breath and cheap cologne. Mac's worry circled on how Watson would act when he came across the two cellphones.

Dixon was playing his role as a true 'by the books' prison guard. He stood to the left of Mac, slightly behind him with a nightstick in his right hand. Dixon had nothing to worry about because his game plan kept him two paces ahead of everyone else. Last night he had given Watson the 411 on the drop being made. He didn't show any concern for Watson shifting through the sheets and towels because he was now down with the team. The OIC was allowed to believe the gold bars on his collar held power.

"Nothing but towels and sheets," Watson informed the OIC minutes later.

Lieutenant Stancil nodded, then reluctantly gave Dixon the go-ahead to remove the cuffs from Mac. No words were exchanged between Mac, Watson, and Dixon until the OIC had left.

"I can't stand his bitch ass!" Dixon muttered. "You good, Mac?"

Mac shrugged, just as Watson slid a towel with his boot across the floor. "Better be glad Stancil didn't have the metal wand detector," Watson mentioned.

Down by Watson's boot lay the two cellphones. If Mac had any doubts toward Watson being down for the hustle, his actions spoke otherwise.

"Was this a random search?" Mac asked Dixon.

"I'll find out."

Mac squatted down by the cart and started shoving the towels and sheets back inside the bag.

"You gotta go to E-block, right?" Dixon asked.

Mac nodded.

"I'll go up in the booth while Watson makes the rounds."

"What about Hart?" Mac wrapped the two cellphones back up. "Will she be up in the booth too?"

"Not to worry. Dixon grinned. "Just stick to the plan 'cause I got my end on point."

The three were out in the hallway five minutes later. Dixon headed off to the control booth while Watson started his rounds in D-block. Mac pushed the OIC out of his mind. The moment came time to hustle, and his mind needed to be focused. He rolled the cart to the door for E-block then waved up to Hart up in the control booth. He could see Dixon up there with her, no doubt flirting. Mac went about his job, picking up the trash and extra sheets and towels that were left out. Since it was lockdown, no inmates were allowed out of their cells. If someone hit their call button, the CO in the booth would call over the radio and inform the floor or block CO to go see what the inmate wanted. Most times their requests were ignored and would just have to wait for the next hourly round.

As Mac neared cell E-15 he saw water seeping from under the door. He sat the loaded bag of sheets and towels on the floor then tapped on cell E-15.

"Yo, bruh, you need a mop?" Mac asked the guy through the door for the sake of anyone that was up and being nosey, Mac played his part in assisting an inmate with a flooded cell. Watson entered the block and Mac sounded the warning.

"Block hot!" Mac shouted, then waved Watson over to where he stood.

"What's up?"

"I need you to open the mop closet. E-15 toilet overflowed."

Watson removed the keys from his belt, then turned and walked toward the mop closet. Everything was planned with the right hand in the dark on the moves the left hand was making. Mac had told the guy in E-15 to pour a few cups of water under his door to make it look like his cell had flooded out.

Watson opened the trap slot on E-15, so Mac could hand the mop through. Everything went down as planned. When Watson headed off to make his rounds, Mac passed some towels through the slot with the two cellphones hidden inside.

Victor L. Martin

At the same time, Hart was up in the booth sliding her mouth up and down Dixon's hard dick. His moans encouraged her to keep going. She flicked her tongue over his balls, then licked his tip twice before sliding him back into her hot mouth.

"Hurry up, baby." He inched his ass closer to the edge of the chair. Hart sped up, taking his dick to the back of her throat. Sex at the workplace remained a fetish to Hart. A fetish she needed to heed as much as possible. As the norm, she happily fondled his balls when his warm nut spurted against the roof of her mouth. A clean towel lay within arm's reach to wipe Dixon down after she was done. By the time she got up off the floor, E-block was clear.

After the smartphones were handed off, Mac went about his business by sweeping the main hallway. Once that was complete, he mopped the floor with cold water in preparation of waxing and buffing. With the wax being laid down, Sergeant Parker had ceased all movement in the hall, so no one would track the floor up. Hart, Dixon, and Watson were up in the booth earning a paycheck by doing nothing. Mac started at the north end of the hall with two coats of wax on the floor. Since he had to wait for the wax to dry, it gave him some rare one-to-one talk with Sergeant Parker. She had a chair out in the hall near her office.

"How are you doing tonight?" She turned her radio down.

"I'm alright. But your boy is an ass."

143

Parker rolled her eyes. "Stancil is not a friend in my book."

"Was it a random search?" Mac sat on the yellow mop bucket.

"Yeah. He's just on a power trip. I was hoping you weren't passing any letters or anything like that. I don't want to see you in no trouble."

Mac smiled. "Lemme find out you care about me."

"And if I do?" She blushed.

"I don't know how to answer that one."

"Can you care about me?"

Mac nodded. "It could happen. But the question is do you want me to."

"I think I do." She smiled at him.

"Okay… you know I can't be in your face every time I see you so let's get on the same page tonight."

"What do you mean by that?"

"I need to know how far you want this… bond between us to go. The main thing we gotta build between us is trust. I got lines I can't cross and you got yours."

"What line won't you cross?"

"I don't snitch… period. Don't ask me 'bout what's going down in the blocks or who doing what, I don't roll like that."

"I respect that, Mac."

"So... why me? Why outta the dudes on this unit, you want me?"

She smiled. "For starters, you're quiet and you don't cause any trouble. Also, you have respect for yourself and towards others and that's a rare trait with guys here."

"How are you with letters? Let's say I have something to share with you, can I put it on paper?"

"As long as you're extra careful and don't—"

"No, I won't put your name on it."

"Guess what?" she whispered. "I forgot to mention one more thing about why I want you to be my secret?"

"What is it?"

"You have a nice dick. I was so turned on when I saw it. To be honest... seeing you naked that night had me upset because I couldn't do anything to you."

"Well, it's for your eyes only."

"So what do you like about me? Are my hips big enough for you?"

Mac didn't make an issue of Parker's bland looks. She wasn't attractive, yet her personality was drawing Mac in. "It's not based on your looks with me, okay? I just wanna be the reason you'll smile when you come up in here."

"That's sweet."

"Nah, it's the truth."

"I think I'm going to really end up liking you."

"Uh, will I be the first inmate you ever dealt with on a personal level?"

She nodded. "In all of my thirteen years on the job, yes, you're the first, Mac." She couldn't tell him the true reason was due to her failing marriage at home. She needed attention, and she yearned to be wanted by a man. Her own husband was no longer attracted to her and it crushed her self-esteem. That night at Mac's door had made her feel valued. If she could, she would tell Mac all of this, but she feared he would not understand.

Mac stood. "I'ma be your first and only."

"I can deal with that. But how long will I have to wait?"

"Wait for what?"

"Until I see you naked again."

"Damn, you get to have all the fun."

"Not so true," she undressed him with her eyes. "I got my ways of finding a private place for us so we can be alone." Her nipples stiffened.

"And do what?"

"Whatever you want to do, if the time is on our side. I don't like to play games nor bite my tongue, Mac."

Hearing those words, Mac knew he had Parker's nose wide open. *Damn, I got this bitch ready to fuck!* With her in his pocket, he would have the keys to the city. *So what she gotta muffin top. I bet that pussy good! Hell, any pussy will be good!*

"When will the floor dry?" she said halting his thoughts.

"'Bout ten minutes, and then I'ma put down one more coat."

Parker stood, then rolled her chair back inside the office. When she backed out of the view of the hallway camera, she motioned Mac inside with her finger. He didn't balk or show any hesitation to enter the office. Once inside, he viewed her at the back of the office unlocking the door that connected to the unit clothes changing area.

"You said the floor with that coat you got down will dry in ten minutes right?" she asked over her shoulder.

"Yeah, fifteen at the max."

Parker pushed the door open, then turned to face Mac. "Good. Because what I want to do will only take half that time."

Mac knew what was up when Parker told him to follow her inside the room. She left the lights out, moving to the corner.

"I know I'm a big girl, Mac. But I'm going on a diet to lose some weight."

Mac went into game mode by taking Parker in his arms and pushing his tongue pass her pink, moist lips. She froze at first, but gave in a heartbeat later, kissing him back. He palmed the mass below her belt that went for her ass while tasting a flavor of peanuts inside her mouth. He had to assure her that he didn't give a fuck how she looked because his position forced him to do so. She moaned softly, reaching down between them to fill her hands with the flesh she yearned for. A breath later she broke from his lips and lowered to a squat. She untucked his shirt then unfastened his pants. A bolt of pleasure tingled his balls the moment she pulled his dick out through his boxers and pants. She stroked him with her soft hands while blowing her hot breath on the top. Mac parted his feet for a better stance, then braced his hands on the wall behind Parker.

"It's so big!" she whispered, before running her tongue along the side of his dick. Parker closed her eyes, moistened her lips then engulfed the thick brown head of Mac's erection. She kept her hands circled around his shaft, slowly easing her lips back and forth.

Behind bars, nine times out of ten, any dealings between an inmate and a prison guard were based on sex. Mac was aware of that fact, which was proven by his dick skating in and out of Parker's mouth. His bond with Parker was sealed a mere four and a half minutes later when she sucked him to a climax. Blowing his mind, she swallowed every drop. In secret.

His mind was set. He would deal with Parker on any level she wanted to take it to. As for telling his secret to Dixon or Watson, fuck no. With them it was business, with Parker it was pleasure but Mac had a plan.

Chapter Fourteen

Back at the strip club in Wilson, Monàe had earned $2,000. At 2:10 a. m. she told Derrick it was time for her to bounce. In truth, she was digging him a ton and his conversation held her attention. She had learned his age, twenty-five, and he had his own place in Kinston.

"I can't believe you're single," Derrick rubbed the back of Monàe's hand.

She lowered her eyes to the table with thoughts of Lorenzo filling her mind. She was missing him, but not to the point of forgiving him for being with another bitch. Her main concern was her son asking about his father.

"I see you don't wanna talk about it, huh?" Derrick read her mood.

She looked up at him from across the table, "I just broke up with him this week, so it's still a fresh hurt."

"I understand. But um… where does that leave us?"

She couldn't lie, she was feeling Derrick. *Shit, I done let this dude play in my kitty on the first night, so I bet he thinks I'm easy. Mmmm… I wouldn't mind getting some dick tonight. Nah, I'll just break myself off with….* She started grinning.

"I say something funny?" Derrick asked.

"No. I was just thinking about something. How about I buy you some breakfast at the Waffle House?"

"If I can have you on my plate, I'm eating till I get full."

She giggled, then told him it was a date. He hid his disappointed when she kindly turned from a kiss he tried to place on her lips. Hiding his crushed ego, he gave her a peck on her cheek and got one more squeeze of her soft ass.

"Give me about ten minutes, and I'll meet you out front by the light pole," she told him. Derrick nodded, then stared at her ass as she strolled out of the VIP booth. His mind was on bagging Monàe's fine ass all to himself. Since talking with her, he realized she wasn't looking for a baller or out to trick for money. Twice he had told her that she didn't belong at the club and if he was her man, he would make sure of it. Of course he wanted the pussy, but for her, he would ride the waiting period out if she planned to act that way. Hell, Tigga found his baby Momma at a strip club so it could be said, strippers need love too.

Ten minutes later, Monàe met Derrick outside the front of the club. She found him leaning against a brand new dark silver Charger resting on 22-inch chrome rims. When she pulled up in her Altima, Derrick hit the remote starter, then slid inside his Charger. He rolled out behind her with the 15-inch subwoofers thumping hard in the trunk. As for Derrick's link with Michelle, it remained unknown to Shayla, but for how long?

***

150

Each new second that Monàe shared with Derrick moved her closer to opening up to him on a personal level. Having broken most of the rules that Michelle had schooled her on, she figured it didn't make any sense to hold back now. While they sat at a corner table by the window inside the Waffle House, she decided to tell him her real name.

"You can call me Shayla from here on out," she poured some maple syrup on her waffles and bacon.

"Now we're moving forward." He grinned. "Maybe next you'll give me your number."

Shayla glanced out the window and pointed at his car. "How much did that set you back?"

"Sixty grand, not including the rims."

"Uhm-huh." She nodded. "And where is it you said you work again?"

Derrick placed his elbows on the table. "C'mon, Shayla, you know I hustle, so I ain't gonna lie."

"And you think it's cool?" She waited for his answer.

"Ain't shit I do against the law is cool. I hustle to eat. I hustle to live and enjoy my life."

"Derrick, I'm feeling your swag, honey. But I can't rock with you and the lifestyle you're living."

"So, you're the one that said you hustle, right?"

Shayla looked confused. "No... well yes," she admitted, knowing he was too good to be true.

"Look, okay. I won't lie to you, so yes, I do hustle like I said, but it's not what you think."

"How do you know what I'm thinking?"

He shrugged. "I guess I'm just assuming."

"You're not very funny." She felt the conversation going south.

"I can when I need to be."

Shayla rolled her eyes, then dug into her plate of food.

"Are you gonna feed me tonight?" He watched her eat.

"Feed you?" She glanced up.

"Yeah, I wanna taste you."

"Boy, please." She shook her head.

"I'm serious, Shayla, I wanna."

"Derrick." She laid her fork down. "I'm trying to eat and you're talking about eating my pussy."

"And?"

"And it makes me think you're crazy."

"Naw it don't. You can't sit there and tell me you don't want to feel my tongue on your clit."

"Derrick!" She playfully kicked his foot under the table.

"Are you gonna feed me or not? No bullshit. Let's cop a room and do it."

"That game is old, okay? You can dead any ideas of getting any pussy tonight. Just because I strip don't make me a hoe."

"Tie me up then."

"What!"

"You heard me. Tie me up and sit on my face or whatever. Damn, I gotta beg to get a taste of you?"

"No, but I know your ass is up to something slick. I don't even know you like that to be going to a room with you."

Derrick figured for sure Shayla was worth his time and effort. Her rejection was only fueling him to push his game even harder. "Okay, maybe you're right. I guess I'm just caught up with your sexy ass. My bad."

"I'll let it slide this time." She smiled.

"Oh, so that means I'll see you again?"

"You might," she teased, lifting her foot up his leg.

Before they two parted ways, Derrick sincerely apologized for his blunt sexual request. Shayla allowed it to ride since she opened the door toward sex by her acts back at the club. She wasn't ashamed of her actions because she had wanted to do it. The money she earned was worth every penny, so tonight was a good one for her.

When she got home she took a shower and slid under the sheets within an hour from walking through the front door. She checked her smartphone for any messages, sadly there were none. Lorenzo took up all of her thoughts. Rolling to her back, she tried to find rest but it was too well hidden. She became restless, tossing and turning under the sheets.

"Fuck it!" she mumbled as she kicked the covers off. She pulled the pink tank-top off, then removed her panties. A minute later her full attention was on the A.E.F. porno featuring Trevon Harrison with two fingers easing in and out of her pussy. If anything could put Shayla to sleep, it was a toe-curling climax.

***

At the same time, Derrick cruised through the hood in Kinston. His Charger rumbled, its strong chrome rims glinting from the street lamps. After he slowed to a stop near the Mitchel Wooten projects, he adjusted the loaded Glock 305 .45 caliber pistol on his lap. He was on his stomping grounds in k-town but refused to get caught slipping on his game. These streets were home to Derrick, and he knew the struggle that each person faced in the hood. His hustle was unique and different, and many had thought of his place to be a waste of time. Pulling from the stop sign, he drove for another three blocks until he stopped in front of a bland looking two-bedroom house with peeling paint and an unkempt yard. A forest green Chrysler 300c sat in the dirt driveway on 22's. Derrick tapped the horn twice before he got out of his ride with the .40 caliber in plain view.

When he reached the rickety porch, a light came on followed by the sound of a deadbolt lock being turned. Derrick was welcomed inside by a young thug gripping a dull black Mossberg 500 pistol grip 20-gauge pump.

"Yo what up, Derrick?" The young thug relaxed his grip on the shotgun as Derrick entered the tiny living room.

"Love and money my dude." Derrick inhaled the strong scent of weed. The space was small, but every piece of furniture was new, along with the 60-inch plasma TV in the corner. "Choppa here?"

"Yeah. In the back wit' a trick."

Derrick shook his head, then made his way down the dark, narrow hall. He stopped at the last door and knocked five times." Choppa, I need to holla atcha!"

Eight seconds later, the door cracked open. Derrick eased inside the dimly lit bedroom that smelled like ass and weed. A butt ass naked chubby girl glanced back at Derrick as she slipped back under the covers.

"Uh, what up?" Choppa sat up in the bed rubbing his eyes.

"What's the deal on your interview? You ain't send me no text or nothing."

Choppa flopped back on the bed. "My bad yo."

"Your bad what? I know you didn't fuck it up!" Derrick shouted.

Choppa sat up quickly. "Nah, it's all good, bruh. I got the job. I just forgot to call you. Well, I did, but you didn't pick up."

Derrick clenched his jaw then eased the door shut behind him. "And who is she?"

"Oh, this is Tori. She's the one I told you about."

"You wanna be down, Tori?" Derrick asked as he made his way to her side of the bed.

"Yeah," she said, excited as Derrick stood over her. When Choppa tugged the sheets down her naked body, her pussy began to throb. She was only twenty-two with two kids and struggling on welfare. Originally from New Bern, she had only been a resident of Kinston for a year and a half. In that time, she had heard all about the PBH crew and how they were getting money. To her surprise, she had never seen any of the five-man crew parted up on a corner or slanging from a trap. She was curious and thirsty for money. Hooking up with Choppa had saved her two months ago. He kept her bills paid and the steady diet of dick was worthy of bragging about. Just last week she was put up on the true hustle with the PBH crew and now she wanted a role in it.

***

Tori didn't trip when Derrick started to undress. In truth, she had wanted to fuck Derrick the first time she saw him, which happened to be the same day she met Choppa. She got up on all fours on the bed with Choppa behind her pushing three fingers in and out of her phat hairy pussy. When Derrick rubbed his dick on her cheek she reached up for it then slid it between her lips. Fucking two men at once wasn't a life changing event for Tori. She sucked gently on Derrick's tool while popping her pussy back against Choppa as he dug her back out. Derrick knew he could mold Tori into a useful pawn for the PBH crew. Closing his eyes, he fucked her warm mouth while thinking of Shayla.

Chapter Fifteen

June 21st, Friday

A week later, Shayla made the short trip to Goldsboro to see what was up with Michelle. Shayla had given up on the failed attempts to reach Michelle via phone and Facebook. Something wasn't right, and Shayla wanted a face-to-face explanation from Michelle instead of hearsay. She was relieved her time nor gas had been wasted when she saw Michelle's BMW parked in front of her townhome.

The cloudless sky greeted Shayla with a bright beam from the sun. She welcomed the high temp in the lower 90ºs and she was dressed appropriately. On her small feet were a pair of green open-toed sandals that showed off her recently pedicure toenails. She wore all white, starting with a thin spaghetti strap halter top and a pair of bright white stretch capri pants. Her hair was pulled back in a simple but sexy ponytail. Lifting her designer shades up on her head she knocked on Michelle's front door with the heat warming her exposed skin.

Michelle was in the kitchen loading the dishwasher when she heard the knock at the front door. Her kids were in the living room watching an animated DVD cartoon but neither would answer the door.

"Mom!" Yasmeen shouted, "Somebody at the door!"

"I can hear that Yasmeen and I'm sure they can hear you outside." Michelle walked barefooted to the door. She *never* invited men to her home so she wasn't stressing her plain appearance today. Her long, brunette hair was parted on top and hung freely pass her shoulders. "Who is it?" she asked reaching the door.

"It's that pretty black girl, Mom!" Yasmeen stood on the sofa with her cute face pressed against the window.

"Yasmeen! Get your behind off the sofa with your shoes on! Haven't I told you not to do that?" Michelle snapped.

"Yes, ma'am," Yasmeen pouted as she jumped back to the floor.

"And the pretty girl has a name and its Shayla, okay. It's not nice to call people out by the color of their skin so don't let me hear you talk like that no more. Now sit back down with your brother and watch TV." Michelle hated to scold her kids but she knew it was needed for them to learn right from wrong. Unlocking the door she forced a smile then welcomed Shayla inside.

"Hey stranger," Shayla said when Michelle motioned her inside.

"Hum, what's up girl?" Michelle closed the door knowing Shayla was going to question her about why she was fired.

"Just wondering why you haven't answered any of my calls," Shayla replied.

"Let's go to the kitchen."

Shayla waved at Yasmeen and Rikeith then followed Michelle to the sunken kitchen. They both took a seat at the glass top kitchen table.

"Wanna get to the point or waste each other's time?" Shayla came right out to get her point across.

Michelle folded her arms, not looking happy. "Yeah I got your text and yes its true about me losing my job."

"For what?"

"I know you heard about it so."

"I'm not going off my assumptions or what I heard. I want you to tell me yourself," Shayla demanded.

Michelle shot a glance toward the living room to make sure Yasmeen wasn't eavesdropping. "I was," she sighed, "caught on film having sex up in the VIP."

"And your reason?"

"Money okay? I broke a guy off for money."

Shayla shook her head. I don't believe that. I mean… why would you take such a risk like that?"

"It don't matter." Michelle shrugged. "I think I wore out my welcome with Shaun anyway."

"Why didn't you return any of my calls? Hell, you even left me at the club without telling me nothing."

"I saw you were already tied up with someone," Michelle replied too fast to conceal the ice in her tone.

"And who would that be?"

Michelle rolled her eyes. "Before I left, I saw you going up to VIP with Derrick."

"I guess I shouldn't be surprised that you know him."

"No, you shouldn't."

"Um… is there something about you two I should know about?"

"He didn't tell you?" Michelle asked.

"No," Shayla replied tersely. "Your name never came up."

"Well, FYI, I got fired because of him."

"Derrick?!" Shayla gasped. "You… had sex with him for money?"

"Yes, I did it, Shayla. Derrick and I got it on up in the VIP. I even enjoyed it to be honest with you. He's a known face at the club and will tell you anything you want to hear for some sex."

Shayla couldn't agree with Michelle. It was clear that Derrick didn't have to say what Michelle wanted to hear. In Shayla's view, he had to pay whatever fee she had requested. Keeping it to herself, Shayla could hear a tone of envy in Michelle's voice.

"Did you give him a lap dance?" Michelle asked dryly.

"Of course, Michelle." Shayla kept a straight face. "What else did you expect me to do up there?"

Michelle unfolded her arms then slid her hands down her face. "I'm tripping, Shayla. I... just... Derrick ain't nothing to me so let's move on to something else. For starters, are you still working at the club?"

"Unfortunately."

"Is something wrong?"

"Nah... I guess I have to catch on to how things work. None of the other girls have been helpful toward me. You were the only one that took the time to tell me anything and that meant a lot to me."

Michelle grinned. "I'm a true friend."

"Yeah. One that didn't return my calls."

"Sorry." Michelle slid back from the table. "I just didn't feel like speaking to no one and plus I was ashamed."

Shayla began to feel sorry for Michelle. "Um, I hope you won't be doing that sex for cash mess no more."

Michelle stood with a frown on her face. "That's behind me."

"Promise?"

"Yes, but—"

"Ain't no buts!" Shayla said as Michelle walked over to reset the cycle on the dishwasher.

"Can you take a mini vacation with me?" Michelle said when she was seated back at the table.

"How are you going on a vacation of any kind with no job?"

"Can you take three days off?"

"Michelle you need to get your life in order. Think about your kids and—"

"Whoa." Michelle raised her hand. "My kids are always on my mind."

Shayla saw the hurt on Michelle's face. "I didn't mean it like that."

"So, will you come with me or not?" Michelle asked crossing her legs under the table.

"My money is still too tight, Michelle. Trust me, if I had it, meaning extra money, my ass wouldn't be stripping that's for damn sure."

"Not even for an all-expense paid vacation?"

"Huh? All-expense paid to where?"

Michelle smiled then leaned across the table. "Guess what?" she whispered.

"Uh, why are you whispering, Michelle?"

"Listen." Michelle waved Shayla closer. "They called me yesterday."

"Who?"

"Janelle and Jurnee!"

When Shayla looked at Michelle with a confused expression it caused Michelle to break the good news.

"Janelle is the CEO of Amatorn Erotic Films and Jurnee is the VP! They want me to go down to Miami for an audition."

It took a second for Michelle's words to sink in with Shayla. "Wait! You mean the porn company called!? The one with Trevon Harrison!?"

Michelle nodded. "Yes! And they encouraged me to bring a friend so I'll feel comfortable. So please… will you come with me?"

Shayla was yelling 'Hell Yeah!' in her mind. At the moment, she was speechless because all she could think about was meeting her fantasy man Trevon in the flesh. "When do we leave?" Shayla asked excitedly.

"Next Monday! Look, I know it's soon, but it's all free! The round trip plane ticket plus the hotel for three nights! Are you really coming with me?"

"Hell to the yeah!"

"You ever been to Miami?"

"Nope. But my ass will be down there next week, you can believe that!"

"Oh yeah," Michelle giggled. "Since we're on the subject of Amatory Erotic Films, um, when were you planning on returning my DVD?"

Now it was Shayla's turn to whisper. She bluntly told Michelle how much she had enjoyed viewing Trevon in action and was now a fan. She also admitted to getting herself off by watching the DVD with the aid of Mr. Tap Out.

"I need to go to the mall to get a new bikini!" Michelle beamed with a wide smile.

"Shit, me too!" Shayla figured she could spend a little of the money Derrick had given her. The trip to Miami had Shayla keyed and ready to leave. The simple idea of meeting Trevon had her buzzing and thinking of his DVD.

***

Lorenzo was missing Shayla, but he couldn't spend a moment without Kahneko's company. For the week Lorenzo had chilled under Travis' roof, Kahneko had shared the bed with him for five nights. Sex was the general part of their rapidly growing friendship. At the moment, she was riding Lorenzo in the lit bedroom with her hands palming his chest.

***

"This my dick," she moaned bouncing herself up and down the warm slick stretch of his dick. Her small breasted jiggled with her snake like twirls of her hips. "Yes! Ohhh Lorenzo... you love my pussy huh?"

Lorenzo was falling deeply for her exotic beauty. For reasons he could not explain, he was again dicking her raw dog. Though she was young, she was experienced in sex. Tilting her head back she moaned out his name while rocking her pussy back and forth. Kahneko wanted Lorenzo to know how she got down. There were no limits for her when it came to fucking. In their short time of knowing each other, sex had been explored with no regrets. Wanting the sex to last through the night, they slowed to change positions.

"What time is it?" Lorenzo asked as Kahneko played with his dick.

"Almost midnight," she replied rolling to her stomach.

Lorenzo sat up, taking a few moments to admire her nice pert ass. He slid his hand over both of her butt cheeks then told her to stand up.

"I wanna try something new." He grinned.

Kahneko felt her pussy throbbing for more of his dick. She was slipping off the bed when suddenly the bedroom door swung open. Lorenzo grabbed the sheets to cover his stiff erection from Mikki's gaze. She waltzed straight up to the bed with her large tits bobbing from side to side. All she had on were a pair of white cotton panties. Lorenzo stared at her large twins, a different pleasure from Kahneko's A-cups.

"You two are making way too much noise!" Mikki slowly grinned. "All you two do is screw."

"Where Travis?" Lorenzo wondered why Mikki was topless in front of him like it was okay.

"He went to the store," Mikki answered.

Lorenzo found it impossible to remove his eyes off of Mikki's beautiful round tits. His stomach turned into a knot when she reached for the sheets.

"Can I see it?" Mikki asked at the same moment of Kahneko easing up behind Lorenzo.

Lorenzo was caught between the two women unsure of what his next move should be.

"Let her see it," Kahneko whispered against his ear. "I'm okay with it."

Lorenzo released the sheets, then stood birth naked in front of Mikki.

"Wow!" Mikki took him in her hands, stroking him up and down. "No wonder you got my girl screaming."

"I told you he had a big dick." Kahneko rubbed her tiny breasts against Lorenzo's arm.

Mikki squeezed Lorenzo's dick then smiled up at him. "Let's go to the living room so we can watch for Travis and have some fun at the same time," Mikki suggested.

"Sounds perfect to me." Kahneko let Lorenzo know it was okay if he hadn't figured it out by now.

Lust pulled Lorenzo into the living room to let the threesome pop off. It began with Mikki on her knees engulfing his wet dick down her throat while Kahneko fondled his balls. Leaving the lights off, he fucked Mikki doggy style on the living room floor, damn near catching an assault charge by the way he was beating the pussy.

Chapter Sixteen

"Wake yo ass up!" Travis barged into the bedroom turning the lights on.

Lorenzo grumbled, tossing the pillow over his head pretending he had been at rest.

"You ain't gonna lay up and fuck all day and night!" Travis joked. "We got some business to handle."

"Hey, Travis," Kahneko smiled with her arms crossed over her breasts. Travis nodded at her then kicked the edge of the bed. "Get up nigga."

Lorenzo sat up frowning, "What the fuck? You know what time it is?"

"Yeah. So get up and get dressed 'cause we got some place to be."

"You serious?" Lorenzo complained with a guilty conscience. Just a mere two minutes ago he was in the living room eating Kahneko's pussy while Mikki rode his dick. The three had broke camp like fleeing refugees when Kahneko spotted Travis' head lights.

"Hell yeah, I'm serious," Travis kept his eyes on as Kahneko as she slipped out of the bed to get dressed. Travis stared hard at Kahneko's nude frame. Her prominent nipples stood out on her chest.

"Where the fuck we 'pose to be going?" Lorenzo asked once Kahneko left the room.

"Wilson," Travis told him. "And it's business."

"At... twelve thirty at night?" Lorenzo got on his feet and pulled up his black Polo jeans.

"I'm driving so it ain't a big deal."

Lorenzo got dressed then met Travis in the living room. Kahneko and Mikki were chatting quietly by the door when Lorenzo looked in their direction. Mikki winked at him, showing her actions would remain in secret. The four exited the cozy apartment and out into the night.

"Call me tomorrow." Kahneko tugged Lorenzo's hand as she stood on the passenger side of Mikki's apple red Infiniti G37 convertible. They shared a brief kiss then broke apart.

Lorenzo was feeling grim when he saw Travis tonguing Mikki on the sidewalk. *Bitches ain't shit! I hope she brushed her teeth... with her bomb ass pussy!* Lorenzo swallowed the secret he now shared with the two Korean freaks. He didn't speak to Travis until they were pulling off in Travis' Cadillac XTS.

"So what's in Wilson?" Lorenzo asked as Travis settled behind the wheel for the trip.

"Club Twerk It," Travis told him with one hand on the wheel.

"Man! Ain't in the mood to be in no strip club. I thought you said it's business."

Travis looked at Lorenzo. "You complain too fuckin' much."

"Whatever, yo," Lorenzo mumbled.

"FYI, we're going to meet somebody and it just happens to be at a strip club. Trust me, business will come first and you'll see that when we get there."

Lorenzo got adjusted in the seat then turned to gaze out the tinted window. There wasn't nothing to see since they were on a dark, unlit, country, back road.

"You still haven't heard from Shayla?" Travis asked with the XTS rolling on cruise control.

Lorenzo sighed. "Nah, not yet."

"Have you tried to call her?"

Lorenzo stared at the dashboard wishing things were different between him and Shayla. Though the sex was good with Kahneko and now Mikki, Lorenzo was missing his girl.

"I take that as a no." Travis came up with his own conclusion when Lorenzo didn't answer. "Look, bruh, just do what you gotta do to get things right between you and Shaya. And don't stress over chillin' at my crib. You're like fam to me so it's all good."

"Thanks, man."

"Besides, I see Kahneko is helping you cope by throwing that million dollar pussy on your ass!"

Lorenzo started grinning from the true statement. "For real my nigga! She got that whoo weee 'tween them legs and that mouth is super!"

"I bet it is since she got you digging up in 'er raw dog."

"Man..." Lorenzo shook his head. "I'm buggin'... like the first day I smashed I was on that Grey Goose and she came on to me hard!"

Travis sucked his teeth. "Aw, nigga you gonna blame it on the alcohol."

"Why not?" Lorenzo laughed. "Jamie Foxx did it first."

They kicked the bullshit back and forth until they reached the strip club in Wilson.

"Pop the glove box and hand me my chain," Travis slowed the XTS to turn at the intersection.

Lorenzo opened the glove box while Travis switched lanes. "Damn!" Lorenzo removed the heavy rose gold chain with a medallion attached. "When you get this? And what does... PBH mean?

"I been had it. And you're about to find out what it means once we get up in the club."

Lorenzo handed Travis his chain with his mind tripping to grasp what was going on. Who would arrange a true business meeting at a strip club, and why was Travis holding back on the 411 on PBH? Lorenzo held his questions in then headed up inside the club. His first shock came when Travis was greeted with VIP treatment at the door.

"You been here before?" Lorenzo inquired while they were being frisked by two dancers.

"Nah. But they knew we were coming. I really don't do no strip clubs. How I look paying a hoe to tease me. Fuck that."

Lorenzo could agree with Travis because he wasn't much of a fan of blowing money on strippers. With that being true, it didn't stop him from lusting over all the phat asses he was greeted with when he stepped through the swinging door. The music was blasting French Montana "Pop That" while a chunky, dark-skinned stripper bounced her baby oil coated ass with the beats. From Lorenzo's point of view, she had to be working with 48 inches of ass that had the club amassed near the stage. Women in form fitting shorts and see-through mesh shirts mingled with men, earning money for their time and attention. Lorenzo couldn't spot one female that he wouldn't fuck.

"C'mon," Travis shouted. "We're going up to VIP. If you see something you like, you can get at 'er later."

***

Lorenzo kept his mouth closed and his eyes open when he made it up the stairs to the VIP floor. It was a new vibe in the greenish lit, upper-status room. The girls even looked better and wore fewer clothes was Lorenzo's first observation. He tried not to stare at a fine topless stripper grinding on a dude's lap in the corner to his left. His attention was hooked at the sight of her cupping her nipples up toward her jeweled tongue. *Mm, I wish Shayla's tits were big enough so she could suck her own nipples,* Lorenzo thought.

"'Bout time you got here!"

Lorenzo stopped behind Travis as a medium built dude stood up behind a table grinning at Travis. Lorenzo quickly noticed the Chris Brown twin also wore a chain just like Travis. P.B.H.

"Ain't like your ass was gonna leave," Travis remarked. "Oh yeah. This my dude I've been telling you about." Travis stepped aside so Lorenzo could stand next to him.

"I heard you've been handling your biz, Lorenzo."

Lorenzo simply nodded.

"Bruh, this my dumb ass cousin, Derrick," Travis laughed.

"Dumb!? You're the one that's 'bout to be going to child support court. Who the fuck you done got knocked up?" Derrick shoved his cousin. "Don't look surprised that I know. Once your mom told mine you might as well posted that shit on Twitter."

"Man, fuck you!" Travis murmured, hating being reminded of his drama with Michelle. He had still not shared a dime of info about her to anyone.

175

"He's on some top secret shit 'bout his seed and baby momma," Lorenzo added his words as Travis flopped down on the seat.

"Probably an old elephant ass ugly trick." Derrick laughed again. "You can't keep 'er ass a secret forever."

Travis glanced at his watch. "I'm here for business... not to talk about no bullshit!"

Derrick ended the worthless chat then motioned Lorenzo to take a seat. They sat in the back of VIP at a small round table near the wall.

"Ya'll drankin' anything?" Derrick asked.

Lorenzo and Travis declined the offer. Travis didn't drink and drive and Lorenzo assumed he couldn't trust himself with any alcohol and all the pussy around him.

"So Lorenzo, my cousin tells me you like trapping behind bars?" Derrick began the conversation. Catching the glance Lorenzo gave Travis, Derrick spoke up again. "I'm not the police... well, some call me that when I go to work just like I'm sure you and Travis are called."

"And how do you know that?" Lorenzo wanted to keep his words at a limit until he knew what the fuck was going on. Cousin or not, he wasn't too pleased about Derrick knowing about his hustle with Travis.

"I work at the Bertie Correctional," Derrick got slick with it. "All of us at the table wear the same uniform and we all got the same hustle."

"Word on what?" Lorenzo doubted heavily.

"This ain't no bullshit," Travis spoke up. "We got shit on lock at Bertie, Maury, Eastern and Johnston is next. This is part of what I was telling you about."

Lorenzo slid closer to the table. "Who's we?" Lorenzo wanted to know.

"PBH. Pretty Boy Hustlers," Derrick answered. "Trust me, bruh, I can't stand the police, but a hustle is a hustle."

Lorenzo looked at Travis. "So... we're like dirty cops... corrupt."

"Call it whatever." Travis shrugged. "We getting bread without having to stand on no corner nor worry 'bout no Jack boys or police kicking the trap door down. You saw the hustle but only the tip of it."

"So who's running this... PBH crew?"

Derrick rubbed his chin. "That ain't important is it? I mean... as long as you're down and eating good then shit shouldn't be a worry, right?"

Lorenzo didn't like Derrick's answer but he knew it wasn't in his favor to start any beef. "Aiight, so how do I fit in?"

"Just keep rolling with Travis 'cause we got some big plans for Maury. Shit 'bout to get real hot but it's all for the good," Derrick explained.

"And I guess I'ma find out about it down the road, huh?"

Derrick glanced at Travis. "You didn't tell 'im?"

Travis slowly shook his head from side to side. "Nah."

Derrick frowned. "Why not? I thought you said you trusted him."

"I do. It's... I figured it was best to wait so calm the fuck down!" Travis looked at his watch to keep his fist from slamming against Derrick's face.

"PBH is serious, Lorenzo. Real talk," Derrick said ignoring the hard stare from his cousin. "We ain't no different from the nigga's on the grind in the trap you feel me? We all 'bout that paper and got clean records and we got guns too. My cousin here," Derrick shot a glare at Travis," was supposed to tell you about a problem that can cause trouble for the PBH crew."

"I'm listening." Lorenzo was hooked.

Derrick held a long gaze at Lorenzo as if he could read his mind. "The internal affairs officer at Eastern Correctional is about to conduct an investigation on a PBH member and we *can't* let that happen."

"Definitively can't let it happen!" Travis added from the side.

Lorenzo had some limited knowledge of what went down when a CO was placed under investigations. If there were strong rumors about a CO doing some bullshit, he or she was moved off the unit to operations. If there was hard proof, the guilty party would be escorted out of the prison. In truth, Lorenzo knew there wasn't much anyone could do once the internal affairs officer was on your ass. "Okay... so you don't want it to happen which I can understand," Lorenzo said in a clear voice. "But what I don't get is how y'all s'pose to stop the investigation."

Travis shifted in his seat. "You know what we gotta do, Lorenzo. Eastern is ringing up damn near ten stacks every six weeks!"

"Whoa. What's all this *we* shit?" Lorenzo pointed out. "Y'all talking all this wild ass shit but ain't nobody really telling me nothing. Now either y'all tell it to me straight... or count me out and that's just keeping it trill."

"He has a point, Derrick." Travis crossed his arms.

"Fuck you mean he has a point!" Derrick bassed. "You're the one that kept him in the dark, so why don't you give it to 'im straight!"

Travis balled up his fist then told Lorenzo what was going down tonight.

"We put a price tag on the internal affairs officer. Like my cousin said, shit is serious with the PBH. We got too much bread on the line to let one muthafucka stop our show."

Lorenzo leaned back from the table. "Y'all nigga's crazy as fuck. Ain't no way I'ma—"

"Nigga you ain't gotta pull no trigger!" Travis exclaimed. "I'm letting you in on something major 'cause I fucks with you hard. Listen, once we handle this issue and you take over the Eastern plug... I promise you'll be sitting on half a mil within a year. We 'bout to turn it up so either you're in or you're out?"

Dollar signs floated before Lorenzo's eyes, blinding him of the risks he was willing to take. *Half a mil... I can breeze with that real lovely.* Lorenzo looked at Derrick's chain. Pretty Boy Hustlers. He had to admit that the hustle was sweet. Small shit, like a gram of coke worth $45-$50 on the street would earn up to $500 behind bars. The promise of a half mil was too tempting for Lorenzo to turn down. He already had a taste of the hustle and it was sweet and easy. Half a mil' was enough to cop Lorenzo's dream ride. A new S-class Benz on 24's. In his greed for money, not once did his son cross his mind. When he told Derrick and Travis he was down for whatever he had no idea that whatever would be seen tonight.

To Be Continued . . .

About the Author

Victor L. Martin is near the end of a nineteen-year bid in the DPS prison system in North Carolina. Pretty Boy Hustlerz is Victor's fourth title with WCP since his debut in 2010 with The Game of Deception. Victor was born in Richmond, VA and raised in Selma, North Carolina and Miami, Florida. Single with no kids allows Victor to place total focus on his career. In the summer of 2018, Victor will regain his freedom, after 19 long years. For more info on Victor L. Martin and his books, please visit his Facebook site by searching for Victor L Martin.

For phone interview request, please contact management at victorlmartin75@gmail.com

For direct contact, please visit his website for his current address.

Facebook – Twitter – Instagram (victorlmartin75)

CPSIA information can be obtained
at www.ICGtesting.com
Printed in the USA
LVOW03s2220131017
552315LV00001B/7/P